UNRECOGNISED
BY THE WORLD AT LARGE

UNRECOGNISED BY THE WORLD AT LARGE

A BIOGRAPHY OF DR HENRY PARSEY MD, PHYSICIAN TO THE HATTON ASYLUM, WARWICK

ALASTAIR ROBSON

Matador
9 Priory Business Park,
Wistow Road, Kibworth Beauchamp,
Leicestershire. LE8 0RX
Tel: 0116 279 2299
Email: books@troubador.co.uk
Web: www.troubador.co.uk/matador
Twitter: @matadorbooks

ISBN 978 1788032 728

British Library Cataloguing in Publication Data.
A catalogue record for this book is available from the British Library.

Printed by TJ International Ltd, Padstow, Cornwall
Typeset in 11pt Aldine401 BT by Troubador Publishing Ltd, Leicester, UK

Matador is an imprint of Troubador Publishing Ltd

MIX
Paper from
responsible sources
FSC® C013056

For Ann, Andrew & Helen

CONTENTS

LIST OF ILLUSTRATIONS

1   Portrait photograph of Dr Henry Parsey (1821–1884).
    frontispiece

2   The first 'Warwick County Asylum' at Stretton-on-Dunsmore.

3   Memorial to Sir Joseph Paxton in the London Road Cemetery, Coventry.

4   Front view of the main entrance to the asylum today.

5   Stratford-upon-Avon's first Dispensary.

6   Warwick's first Dispensary.

7   Silver salver presented by the Mayor of Stratford-upon-Avon to Dr John Conolly.

8   Silver Testimonial presented to Dr John Conolly.

9   Bronze bust of Dr John Conolly.

10 Tomb of Sir John Bucknill at Clifton-on-Dunsmore, Warwickshire.

11 Architect's drawing of the proposed 'Warneford General Bathing Institution and Leamington Hospital'.

12 Warneford Medal awarded to Henry Parsey by King's College, University of London (June 1838).

13 Dr Parsey's carriage outside the main entrance to the asylum.

14 Memorial window in Holy Trinity Church, Hatton.

15 Photograph of Dr Alfred Miller MB, Medical Superintendent of the Hatton asylum from 1891-1923.

16 Wooden panel in memory of Dr Alfred Miller.

SOURCE OF ILLUSTRATIONS: 1, 3, 4, 5, 6, 9, 12, 14, 16 Author's photograph; 2 photograph courtesy of Dr Anne Langley; 7, 8 photographs courtesy of Auckland Art Gallery Toi a Tamaki, New Zealand; 10 photograph courtesy of the Royal College of Physicians, London; 11 private collection, photograph courtesy of Mr Norman Hyde; 13, 15 photographs [CR 2653/114; CR 2653/116] courtesy of County Records Office, Warwick.

AUTHOR'S NOTE

This study uses medical terms found in the historical records of the Warwick Asylum and other contemporary writings which may be considered derogatory or offensive to present day readers.

Such terms had specific usage and were commonly used by physicians – and the general public – of the Victorian era.

A glossary of these terms with their definitions in the Victorian context is appended.

ACKNOWLEDGEMENTS

I would like to thank firstly Mrs Ann McKenzie (Dr Parsey's great-granddaughter) and her husband Ian for their encouragement when I first approached them regarding writing a biography of Dr Henry Parsey and for making available to me personal information and such papers and personal effects of his that still remain in the family's possession. Without their co-operation, this study of his life would have been very limited indeed.

My thanks are also due to the staff of the County Records Office, Warwick, for their help in obtaining numerous documents from the archive of the Hatton asylum; to Francis Maunze, Librarian at the Royal College of Psychiatrists, for, granting me access to the College's Library; to Dr Andy Owen, Consultant Psychiatrist, who introduced me to the small collection of artefacts from the Hatton asylum which have been preserved in St Michael's Hospital, Warwick; regrettably most of the asylum's library and other various book collections of its Medical Superintendents have been dispersed.

Sincere acknowledgement must be given to the late Dr Peter Beckett MD, cousin of Samuel and graduate of Trinity College, Dublin, who then trained in psychiatry in Detroit, returning to the School of Physic in 1969 – together with a somewhat disconcerting mid-West American accent – as its first Professor of Psychiatry. His excellent clinical teaching inspired many of his students, including myself, to take a special interest in his subject. His unexpected death at the age of 51, after only six years in post, was a very great loss indeed to the medical school.

Finally, special thanks are due, of course, to my wife Ann, for accompanying me enthusiastically on numerous visits to churches, tombs and other buildings, and also for her longstanding patience whilst this book was being written.

A. M. R.
Warwickshire
4 May 2016

INTRODUCTION

I was never actually inside the Hatton asylum myself. The closest I came to being so was when playing cricket for the local GPs in matches on the asylum's idiosyncratic cricket ground during the very last years of its admitting patients.[1] I did send a number of patients into it, however, during my years in practice. It was usual for them to be admitted to Parsey Ward: whilst completing the necessary paperwork, I occasionally wondered who the admission ward was named after.

I discovered that it was Dr Henry Parsey, the asylum's first Medical Superintendent, who had been widely respected by his contemporaries for the excellence of the care he provided for his patients.

One of his obituarists regretted 'that he had been unrecognized by the world at large',[2] (which I have taken for the title of this book), for his professional and personal qualities, and another regretted that 'he did not place much on permanent record in the literature of the subject in which he was so skilled'.[3]

It is also regrettable that so few of his personal papers have survived, but there proved to be enough material available for this study of Dr Parsey's life and the world of the Hatton asylum, which will, I hope, convey to readers why it was his contemporaries held him, and the asylum, in such high esteem.

NOTES

1. The cricket ground, in front of the asylum, had an excellent square – allegedly laid by patients under the supervision of the WCCC head groundsman – but the ground itself, being saucer-shaped, made batting unusually onerous in that stroking the ball to the boundary required real effort.
2. Obituary of WHP in *The Lancet*, quoted in *Royal Leamington Spa Courier* 26 January 1884.
3. Obituary of WHP, *The B J Psych* 1884, 30 (129) 166.

CHAPTER 1

CARE OF THE INSANE BEFORE
THE COUNTY ASYLUM ACT OF 1845

*The site chosen for its commanding and beautiful prospects is such that
cannot fail to impress everyone with its desirableness.*

*From every window in the galleries and day rooms a large extent
of the surrounding country is visible, and the walls around the airing
courts, that would otherwise obstruct the view from them, being sunk
in ha-has, the fullest possible advantage has been taken of that formerly
neglected but useful and important adjunct in the treatment of insanity,
the pleasing calm influence of rich and beautiful scenery.*[1]

This description of the new asylum at Hatton, by Dr Henry
Parsey, its first Medical Superintendent, is taken from his
annual report of 1856 to the Committee of Visitors, written
some four years after it had opened to receive patients.

'The Warwick County Lunatic Asylum', to give it its full
title – or 'Hatton asylum', as it was more colloquially known –
was one of a number of new asylums appearing in England at
the time, and which were being heralded as ideal institutions
for the care – and, hopefully, cure – of the mentally ill.

Sir George Paget, Regius Professor of Physic at
Cambridge University, in his Harveian Oration to the
Members of the Royal College of Physicians in 1866
considered that:

1

A pauper lunatic asylum, such as may now be seen in our English counties, is the most blessed manifestation of true civilization that the world can present.

However, half a century earlier, asylums were not viewed in this light at all; it was then still common practice to employ physical restraint in the treatment (so to speak) of the insane:

When an unruly patient enters a common lunatic house, he is bled, dressed in a straight waistcoat, has his head shaved, is subjected to the showerbath, put upon a low diet, kept in darkness and compelled to swallow some active purgative medicine. If measures of this kind do not effect any amendment, the medical resources of the establishment are at an end.[2]

Until the middle of the nineteenth century, treatment of the insane might have been pretty ghastly in England, but it was so much worse everywhere else:

In some parts of the Continent the insane are mixed with criminals, shut up in damp cells, the windows of which are unglazed, furnished with beds of straw, but perfectly naked…they are fed once a day, the food being thrown to them through the bars, as carrion is tossed to a wolf.[3]

Before 1800, asylums for the insane were few and far between: the best known, and the largest, was the Hospital of St Mary of Bethlehem in London, known as 'Bethlem Hospital' – or just 'Bedlam'.[4] The hospital had been founded by monks as a Priory in Bishopsgate in 1247 as a medieval 'hospice', initially caring for the halt and the lame, and offering shelter to travellers and later on to a limited number of lunatics.[5]

If lunatics were manageable, then they would have remained within the family, sometimes being capable of menial tasks inside or outside the house, sometimes not; the 'village idiot' was a common sight, tolerated in rural communities. If more difficult to manage, then – if family finances allowed – they might have been boarded out in 'madhouses', or even sent abroad. If truly unmanageable, then they would probably have been kept inside the house or in an outbuilding under some form of physical restraint, or merely left to wander the highways and bye-ways to beg, like 'Tom o' Bedlam' in Shakespeare's 'King Lear'.

John Aubrey, the antiquary, wrote of 'Bedlamites' (as they were also known) in 1656:

Till the breaking out of the Civill Warres, Tom o' Bedlams did travel about the countrey. They had been poore distracted men that had been put in Bedlam, where, recovering to some sobernesse, they were licentiated to goe a-begging...[6]

Unlicensed lunatics would eventually find themselves, through vagrancy, confined in one institution or another – with minor criminals in a house of correction (if the misdemeanour was trivial) or gaol (if they tried the Justices' patience sorely) or in a workhouse – all of which used physical restraint, to a greater or lesser degree, to manage them.

To accommodate the increasing numbers of lunatics, Bethlem hospital moved to Moorfields in 1676. 'New Bethlem' was considered to be extremely elegant (from the exterior at least); the building having apparently been designed in the style of the Tuileries in Paris (allegedly much to King Louis XIV's discomfiture).[7]

Within the building, accommodation for the (now) one hundred inmates was Spartan in the extreme. And Hogarth's graphic – but accurate – depiction in 1733 of the hospital's ward for incurable males in his painting 'The Rake in Bedlam' – the final scene in a series of eight paintings titled 'The Rake's Progress'[8] – together with the Hospital's policy of providing regular tours of the wards to the public, at a charge, to view the inmates for entertainment, which continued until 1770, hardly lessened the hospital's reputation for callous treatment.[9]

Neither can this reputation have been assuaged in any way by the two large statues in Portland stone above the entrance gates to the hospital, known as the 'brainless brothers' – on the one side 'Melancholy' and on the other 'Raving Madness' (graphically portrayed with shaven head and restrained, of course, by chains and manacles).[10]

'New Bethlem' accepted 'all persons of unsound mind, presumed to be curable' as patients, but those who remained insane for more than twelve months following admission were deemed 'uncured' and were discharged either back to their families, or to privately run 'mad-houses', or, as a last resort, to survive as best they could on the streets by begging: the hospital later built 'long-stay' wards in an attempt to reduce the number of 'uncured' patients discharged homeless, but competition for these beds was fierce.

The general public became much more aware of mental illness during King George III's first lapse into insanity in November 1788, when regular bulletins on the King's illness were given to Parish churches, containing prayers for his speedy recovery to be said by congregations.

However, the medical treatment that George III received from the Reverend Dr Francis Willis[11] – a clergyman with an Oxford medical degree, a small private asylum in Lincolnshire, and a reputation as a 'mad-doctor' for curing lunatics – of being restrained by being strapped into a robust 'coercion chair' whilst in a straight-jacket, gagged, and spoken to in a manner deliberately designed 'to inculcate salutary fear'[12] – presumably in an attempt to terrify the patient into his wits – was not made widely known.

The Monarch had to receive the best treatment available, of course, and Dr Willis with his accoutrements of restraint – the better to allow the King to listen to Dr Willis's lectures on self-control – were considered to be the best available treatment. The broadsheets of the day took a less sanguine view of the treatment meted out:

> *The King employs three doctors daily,*
> *Willis, Heberden[13] and Baillie[14],*
> *All exceedingly clever men,*
> *Baillie, Willis and Heberden,*
> *But doubtful which most sure to kill is,*
> *Baillie, Heberden or Willis.*

It is probable, however, that George III's illness was in fact physical rather than mental: it is very likely that he suffered from porphyria, an inherited metabolic condition that manifests itself in episodes of acute abdominal pain, with physical features (especially blue urine in acute attacks), together with irritability, confusion or other florid psychiatric symptoms. Be that as it may, the King eventually recovered his wits, in spite of treatment received.

On 23 April 1779, St George's Day, the King attended a Service of Thanksgiving for his recovery in St Paul's Cathedral and there was general rejoicing, his subjects holding similar services in churches throughout the land. Indeed, the 4th Lord Aylesford, of Packington Hall in Warwickshire, celebrated his Monarch's recovery by building on his estate one of the finest Italianate churches in England – St James's Church, Great Packington.[15]

The King presented Dr Willis with a gold watch,

Parliament voted him a pension of £1000 a year for twenty-one years – he was then in his 70s – and he returned to supervising his 'mad-house' in Lincolnshire.[16]

The wide circulation of prints of Hogarth's 'Rake's Progress' paintings had publicized that asylum care in the era of restraint was not particularly salubrious, and after the treatment which George III had received became widely known, public opinion was very much more intolerant of restraint as a treatment of the insane, of 'mad-houses' in general, and also of those who cared (if that is the correct word) for the insane for financial gain.

When the Parliamentary Committee on Madhouses in 1815 was informed of the care an inpatient by the name of James Norris had received in Bethlem Hospital, there was a public furore:

A stout ring was riveted round his neck. Round his body a strong iron bar, about two inches wide was riveted; on each side of the bar was a circular projection, which being fashioned to and enclosing each of his arms, pinioned them close to his sides. The waist bar was secured by two similar bars, which, passing over his shoulders, were riveted to the waist bar both before and behind. The iron ring round his neck was connected to his shoulders by a double link. From each of these bars another chain passed to the ring on the upright bar. His right leg was chained to the trough, in which he had remained thus encaged and enchained twelve years. During the whole of this period it was impossible for him, from the nature of the restraint in which he was placed, either to stand quite upright or to lie down at ease.[17]

Diagnosed as 'dangerous and incurable', Norris was violent and had once stabbed an (allegedly) intoxicated keeper who had been attempting to restrain him. The governors of Bethlem decided he needed further restraint, and considered the mechanism used was humane, as it 'caused him no pain, and allowed him to feed himself, to keep himself clean, and to assist himself in the ordinary evacuations of nature'.

When they were asked the reason for putting him in irons, their reply was that 'it would require a larger expense than they could afford to keep servants to take care of him if he was not ironed'. The governors seemed surprised when the Royal Commission considered this treatment inhumane in the extreme: in their defence they stated that Norris had been supplied with books and paper, read extensively, and was allowed a pet cat as a companion (all the better to help to control vermin within his cell) by his current keeper, who seems to have been a relatively compassionate individual.

Needless to say, Norris was removed from the contraption, only to die within months: the official cause of death was tuberculosis, but it may well have been that he died from intestinal obstruction due to constipation, a likely consequence of such prolonged immobility. When this degree of coercion and other instances of severe neglect within the asylum were made public, Dr Thomas Monro, a member of the Royal College of Physicians and the third of four generations of the Monro family to be Principal Physician at Bethlem Hospital, resigned his post in 1816, following the Inquiry's criticism of his 'wanting in humanity' towards his patients.

He was succeeded as Principal Physician by his son, Dr Edward Monro: it was said by wags in the coffee houses that the only change that had occurred in Bethlem as a result of the Inquiry was the Christian name of the Dr Monro in charge.[18]

Abolition of restraint (for the greater part) in Bethlem would have to await the arrival of Dr William Charles Hood[19] as Principal Physician in 1853, under whom standards of care in Bethlem would become exemplary: Dr Henry Parsey was to speak highly of the care the hospital provided, in his report to the Visitors of the Hatton asylum in 1864.

★

Mention must be made of St Luke's Hospital for Lunatics, founded in 1751, (not to be confused with St Luke's Hospital for the Clergy in Fitzroy Square). The second hospital to be built in London to care for lunatics, it was founded as a more humane alternative to Bethlem, where there would be privacy and no public display of patients, who were mostly from the middle classes. Its first physician was Dr William Battie, the only physician to be elected President of the Royal College of Physicians whose practice was in lunacy (and whose name, corrupted to 'batty', entered the language as a synonym for 'crazy'). Its first site was in Moorfields, close to Bethlem Hospital, but in 1786 it moved to a new building on City Road, which had a magnificent frontage, five hundred feet in length, and was considered to be one of the finest buildings in London of its time.[20]

But the accommodation it provided for some three hundred patients, segregated by sex into two wings, continued to be of a Spartan nature with single cells, high set unglazed windows, no heating (lunatics were considered to be impervious to the cold) and straw on wooden bedsteads. Treatment, whilst superficially perhaps more humane than that in Bethlem, still involved bleeding, emetics, purgatives, and cold plunge baths in the basement, all ancient treatments for insanity.

But in 1864 Dr Henry Parsey was also to speak highly of the quality of care St Luke's then provided, recommending the institution for the care of the insane of the Victorian lower middle and middle class who, when insane, were very poorly provided for, compared with paupers.

★

The concept of care – rather than confinement – for the mentally ill originated in France in the late eighteenth century. Auguste Pinel, the doctor in charge of the Bicêtre Hospital for male lunatics in Paris, and his assistant Jean-Etienne Esquirol, realized that treating the mentally ill with care and consideration resulted in considerably better behaviour than that achieved by locking them up and – literally – throwing away the key.[21] This is an account of Pinel's first release of a patient from restraint:

The first man to be unchained by Pinel in the Bicêtre was an English captain, whose history no-one knew, as he had been in chains for over forty years. He was thought to be one of the most furious among them; his keepers approached him with caution, as he had in a fit of fury killed one of them on the spot with a blow from his manacles. Pinel was unattended, and calmly said to him 'Captain, I will order your chains to be taken off, and give you liberty to walk in the court, if you will promise me to behave well and injure no-one.'

'Yes, I promise you,' said the maniac; 'but you are laughing at me; you are all too much afraid of me'.

'I have six men', answered Pinel, 'ready to enforce my commands, if necessary. Believe me that on my word, I will give you your liberty if you will put on this waistcoat.'

He submitted to this willingly, without a word; his chains were removed, and the keepers retired, leaving the door of the cell open. He raised himself many times from the seat, but fell again on it, for he had been in a sitting posture so long that he had lost the use of his legs; in a quarter of an hour he succeeded in maintaining his balance, and with tottering steps came to the door of his dark cell. His first look was at the sky, and he cried out enthusiastically, 'How beautiful!'.

During the rest of the day he was constantly in motion, walking up and down the staircases, and uttering exclamations of delight. In the evening he returned of his own accord into his cell, where a better bed than he had been accustomed to had been prepared for him, and he slept tranquilly.

During the two successive years which he spent in the Bicêtre, he had no return of his previous paroxysms, but even rendered himself useful, by exercising a kind of authority over the insane patients, whom he ruled in his own fashion.

In the course of a few days, Pinel released fifty-three maniacs from their chains; among them were men of all conditions and countries; workmen, merchants, soldiers, lawyers &c. The result was beyond his hopes. Tranquility and harmony succeeded to tumult and disorder, and the whole discipline was marked with a regularity and kindness which had the most favourable effect on the insane themselves, rendering even the most furious more tractable.[22]

Pinel described this approach of non-restraint as 'traitement moral'; he considered persons suffering from 'mental alienation' required treatment from an 'alienist' (one who treats mental alienation) who had perspicacity, a talent for observation, intelligence, goodwill, perseverance, patience, experience, an imposing physique, and a countenance that commands respect. Personal qualities still expected of every medical graduate today, surely?

'Traitement moral' came to be adopted widely in English asylums by the middle of the nineteenth century, where it was known as 'moral management', following the pioneering work at 'The Retreat' at York.

'The Retreat' was a small purpose-built institution which had been opened in 1796 by William Tuke, not a doctor but a retired tea merchant and Quaker, 'for insane persons of the Society of Friends'. He wanted to provide accommodation where they would be treated with benevolence and personal attention. Patients could wear their own clothing and were allowed to come and go within the house and grounds, with the aim of restoring their self-respect; albeit with a judicious use of the darkened room and the straightjacket if need be.

In 1838, in a small asylum in Lincoln, Dr Robert Gardiner Hill was the first doctor to abolish restraint completely in a public asylum in England:

> *I wish to complete that which Pinel began. I assert then in plain and distinct terms, that in a properly constructed building, with a sufficient number of suitable attendants, restraint is never necessary, never justifiable and always injurious, in all cases of lunacy whatsoever.*[23]

Dr John Conolly, at that time in general medical practice in Warwickshire, but shortly to take up the post of Resident Physician at the Middlesex County Asylum at Hanwell, visited Gardiner Hill in his Lincoln asylum to witness 'moral management' with a total lack of the use of restraint of patients in practice.

Astonishingly, for a physician with no previous experience of managing any form of asylum, within three months of his arrival in Hanwell in 1839, Conolly had likewise removed all forms of mechanical restraint from the eight hundred and three patients therein. He was to write in 1842:

> *The management of a large asylum is not only practicable without the application of bodily coercion to the patients, but that, after the total disuse of such a method of control, the whole character of an asylum undergoes a gradual and beneficial change.*[24]

Other British alienists began to apply Conolly's regime of non-restraint in their asylums, including Dr John Bucknill, on his appointment in 1841 as the Medical Superintendent at the new Devon County Asylum in Exminster, where he was to be joined five years later by Henry Parsey, as his first Medical Assistant.

The introduction of 'moral management' transformed treatment of the insane; by the middle of the century, the regime for admitting new patients to an asylum bore absolutely no relation to the previous procedures of being bled, having one's head shaved, being introduced to the straight-waistcoat and being subjected to the forcible administration of aperients:

The patient should be received and welcomed kindly and relieved from alarm or anxiety, by being reassured that no unkindness will be experienced, and that being admitted to the asylum will lead to recovery, or to improved health and comfort.

The undressing of patients should be done gently and kindly and each patient should have a warm bath; and it must be remembered, that this luxury is so entirely new to most of the poorer patients as to be by no means welcome to them...It is gratifying, after the patient has been an hour in the asylum to see a poor, ragged, dirty, half-starved, sullen, wretched creature transformed into a clean, decently-dressed, cheerful and hopeful person, disposed to be pleased with everybody and this is a first step towards cure.[25]

By 1845 it would be a statutory requirement in England & Wales that no patient be struck or kept in perpetual restraint or seclusion, and that no patient be restrained or secluded at any time, except by medical authority, or kept in restraint or seclusion longer than is absolutely necessary.[26]

The Rev Dr Francis Willis's era of management of the insane by 'the inculcation of salutary fear' – together with the necessary accoutrements – was over.

ENDNOTES

1. WHP *Annual Report 1856*
2. Conolly *Indications of Insanity* p15
3. Browne *What Asylums Were, Are and Ought to Be* p112
4. 'Bedlam' = 'scene of uproar' [COD]
5. The hospital regularly sent monks into the city as 'basket men' to beg for food and clothing for the inmates: hence lunatics were known as 'basket cases'.
6. In Aubrey *A Natural History of Wiltshire* 1847 edition p 93; quoted in Jones *Asylums and After* p7. John Aubrey (1626-1697); antiquary and author of *'Brief Lives'*, a collection of entertaining, and occasionally scurrilous, short biographical vignettes of his contemporaries.
7. Jones *Asylums and After* p 9.
8. Engravings of the original paintings, now on display in Sir John Soane's Museum in London were published and widely circulated.
9. There were two further moves; the second was to Southwark in 1815 and finally to Beckenham, Kent in 1930 where it still functions as a psychiatric hospital. The central block of the Southwark building became the Imperial War Museum in 1936.
10. *"O'er the gates of Bedlam, by his fam'd father's hand,*
    Great Cibber's brazen brainless brothers stand."
    From *'The Dunciad'* (Book 1) by Alexander Pope (1688-1744), satirical poet. These statues are now on display in the 'Bethlem Museum of the Mind' at the Maudsley Hospital, Beckenham.
11. Francis Willis (1718-1807) q Oxford; he was descended from the Willis family of Fenny Compton, Warwickshire.
12. Quoted in Macalpine & Hunter *George III and the Mad Business* p275.
13. William Heberden MD (1767-1845) q Oxford; physician to George III.
14. Matthew Baillie MD (1761-1823) q Oxford; physician to

George III. His uncle, John Hunter, the eminent surgeon, bequeathed to him his house and personal anatomical museum, which is now housed in the Royal College of Surgeons, Lincoln's Inn, London.

15. The organ, built to the specification of GF Handel in 1749, is a later addition, and originally came from Gopsall Hall in Leicestershire (now demolished), the home of his librettist, Charles Jennens.

16. Francis Willis died in his asylum at Greatford Hall in Lincolnshire on 5 December 1807, in his 90th year. A bust of him by the British sculptor Joseph Nollekens (1737-1823) can be seen in the adjacent church of St Thomas à Becket. George III eventually died insane in Windsor Castle in 1820, aged 81.

17. Quoted in Andrews & Scull *Undertaker of the Mind* p274.

18. The four members of the Monro family, all Fellows of the Royal College of Physicians, who became successively Physicians to Bethlem Hospital for a total of 128 years were firstly James Monro (1728-1752); his son John (1752-1783); his grandson Thomas (1816); and his great-grandson Edward (1816-1856).

19. b 1824. Attended TCD and Guy's Hospital. MD St Andrew's 1846. Resigned from Bethlem in 1862 to join John Bucknill as a Lord Chancellor's Visitor in Lunacy. Knighted 1868, d 1870.

20. Late in its life it was used by the Bank of England to print banknotes, but it was eventually demolished in 1961.

21. The Bicêtre Hospice (for men) and the Salpetrière Hospice (for women), both founded by King Louis XIV, were Paris's two large institutions which provided custodial care for a mixture of the physically and mentally sick and the criminal.

22. Conolly *On The Construction and Government of Lunatic Asylums* p165

23. Gardiner Hill *The Total Abolition of Personal Restraint* p153-4.

24. Conolly Fourth Annual Report 1842 to Hanwell Visitors, quoted in Clark *A Memoir of John Conolly* p26.

25. Conolly *On the Construction and Government of Lunatic Asylums*

26. Lunacy Act 1845 (8 & 9 Vict. c. 126).

CHAPTER 2

BUILDING THE ASYLUM

If the Lunacy Act and the County Asylums Act of 1845 had not passed into the statute book, it is doubtful if the Hatton asylum – or more correctly, the County Lunatic Asylum, Warwick – would ever have been built at all.

An earlier Parliamentary Act of 1828 had given discretionary powers to each County to build such an establishment for pauper lunatics, but not all did so; in 1845 there were still eleven Counties (including Warwickshire) in England and ten in Wales without a County Asylum.

The 1845 County Asylums Act 'for the regulation of lunatic asylums' made it compulsory for each county in England & Wales, (but not Scotland where, as ever, they did things differently), to provide accommodation and treatment – such as it was – for pauper lunatics, within three years. Some counties pooled their resources together and provided a single asylum for their insane, such as the Three Counties Asylum in Bedfordshire, which opened in 1860 and provided four hundred beds for patients from Bedfordshire, Hertfordshire and Huntingdonshire, but it was not until 1862, with the opening of the Cumberland & Westmoreland Asylum in Carlisle, that every county had complied.

The compulsory edict of the 1845 Act provoked the Warwickshire Justices into action regarding building an asylum, and in 1846 a Committee was formed at the Midsummer Quarter Sessions, as the law dictated, to oversee the building and administration of a new asylum for the County's pauper lunatics.

The 1845 Lunacy Act 'for the better care and treatment of lunatics in England and Wales', gave the Commissioners in Lunacy, who were a body of six salaried fulltime members, three medical and three legal, together with five honorary part-time lay members, authority over all the asylums in England and Wales – apart from Bethlem Hospital – reporting to the Lord Chancellor.

The Commissioners in Lunacy had been formed by the Lunacy Act of 1842, and their Chairman was Anthony Astley Cooper – later 7th Earl of Shaftesbury – who was a lifelong champion for reform of the care of lunatics.

The Commissioners had to approve all designs for proposed asylums and were responsible for their regulation and had to be notified of all admissions and discharges of patients from the asylums. Statutory requirements were very detailed indeed.

The 'Committee of Visitors' were Justices of the Peace and other eminent local men who supervised the administration of an asylum, rather like a Board of Governors. By statute they were obliged

> to visit the asylum every three months and see and examine, as far as circumstances will permit, every lunatic therein, and the order and [medical] certificate for the admission of every lunatic admitted since the last visitation of the visitors [...] and be accompanied by the physician of the asylum.

A House Committee met monthly at the asylum 'for the purpose of making a more frequent and minute investigation into the details of management, the bodily and mental condition of the patients, the regularity of all journals, of all certificates and other documents, and of all accounts'.

Warwickshire had delayed providing an asylum because the County had previously made provision for the care of its lunatic population – be they pauper, middle class or aristocrat – via 'mad-houses'. These were private houses, licensed by the Justices at Quarter Sessions and regularly inspected, somewhat cursorily perhaps, by an approved medical officer and two Justices of the Peace.

'Mad-houses' were available as an option for those with means, although parishes would sometimes send there their more difficult pauper lunatics; for the most part they were private houses which were merely boarding-houses for the more manageable insane and were run for profit by clergymen, or doctors of one sort or another, or simply by unqualified 'proprietors', some of whom were plainly unsuited to the task and some of whom had a reputation for accepting patients with very dubious medical certification indeed.

False imprisonment in private 'mad-houses' had always been a matter for concern by the public, rightly or wrongly, and it was not until the Madhouses Act 1828 that an order for committal of a non-pauper to a licensed madhouse required a relative's authorization in writing and two medical certificates and, for a pauper, an order from two Justices of the Peace [reduced to one in 1832], or an Overseer of the Poor (manager of a workhouse) and the officiating clergyman of the Parish, plus one medical certificate.

John Conolly, giving evidence before the House of Commons Select Committee on Care and Treatment of Lunatics, in 1859, referring to his five years as the 'Inspecting Physician of the lunatic houses of the County of Warwickshire', commented:

The class of people taking care of lunatics has, within my own experience, very much improved. I remember when almost every man who kept an asylum was an eccentric, or had something peculiar about him, or strange in his appearance, and was more calculated to knock a patient down than to cure him.

THE FIRST COUNTY ASYLUM

The new Warwick County Asylum, on which so much energy was now being bestowed by the Justices, was not the first 'County Asylum' in Warwickshire. An asylum had opened some years earlier, in 1818, in Stretton-on-Dunsmore, but for a very different purpose; its full title was the 'Warwick County Asylum for Juvenile Delinquents'. It provided accommodation for boys aged from fourteen to sixteen who were convicted criminals, giving them employment for two years making shoes and clothing and being taught to read and write. It was supported by voluntary contribution and housed up to fifteen boys.[1]

It was the first reformatory to be established outside London. There was 'no coercion beyond giving the boys a flogging now and then'; moral management was its philosophy, and it had a visiting chaplain to help further these aims.

Some 175 boys passed through the asylum before its closure in 1856, and of those, about ten percent had been dismissed for unruly behaviour, and about a quarter had reoffended; (twice that number of boys merely released from prison went on to reoffend).

After two years the boys were found work by the Master, mostly with tailors or shoemakers, but some others were placed with a gardener, a cooper, a glazier, a grocer etc., probably as apprentices, and a number entered the military forces.

The reformatory asylum building is now a farmhouse, but is still recognizable as having once been an institution by the absence of windows in the back of the three storey house, thought possibly to have been a security measure to prevent boys from absconding.[2]

MADHOUSES

The County had seven other mad-houses of varying capacities; more than any other English County. Henley-in-Arden had four, three of which having been established in the 1700s, which lent the town a somewhat notorious reputation.

Hunningham House was the largest, accommodating more than seventy inmates, but one, owned in 1867 by a Dr Dartnell, (a retired Deputy Inspector of Army hospitals), was a substantial two storied building with five acres of elegant gardens, which was licensed for six residents and provided accommodation by being converted into two apartments: one with a drawing room, dining room and private sitting room etc., for five males, and the second apartment accommodated a single female who lived with Dr Dartnell and his family. Plainly a residence for a monied middle-class clientele, as was Watchbury House asylum, at Barford, which accommodated – 'with the necessary care and restraint' – eight 'patients of respectability of either sex'.

Most of the houses were licensed for up to ten residents, but usually housed fewer, in accommodation very much like a ordinary middle class home, although the larger houses that were licensed for 30 residents or more – Hunningham House, for example – provided some accommodation in converted stables and outbuildings.[3]

By way of comparison, Brislington House, near Bristol,

a purpose-built private lunatic asylum for those who could afford private care for their relatives, was set in five hundred acres, kept greyhounds for the amusement of the patients, had an aviary with pheasants, a bowling green, a pagoda, a summer house in the pleasure gardens and some patients kept their own carriages and horses. Yet they were still put into straightjackets, when circumstances so demanded, it was alleged.[4]

THE HATTON ASYLUM

The County Lunatic Asylum's Committee of Visitors first met at Judge's House, Warwick on Wednesday, 22 July 1846. It was comprised of twenty-one members, which included Sir Thomas George Skipwith, Bt., The Lord Leigh, several Esquires, and six Clergymen, including the Rev Charles Pilkington, Vicar of Stockton.

The Commissioners in Lunacy in 1847 had issued detailed 'Rules to be Observed with Reference to the Selection of the Site of an Asylum'. The Committee commenced its duties by looking for a suitable site.

Negotiations proceeded apace: on 17 May 1847, after consideration of a number of possible sites within 5 miles of Warwick town,[5] a contract was drawn up between the Committee and the Earl of Warwick 'for the purchase of about 36 acres of land in the Parishes of Hatton and Budbrooke distant about 2 miles from the Town of Warwick [this was, in essence, the Earl of Warwick's deer park] at the sum of £4802, including the timber for the purposes of the intended asylum, an abundant supply of good water having been first ascertained'.

The asylum's final position was dictated, for the greater part, by the finding by bore hole of an adequate supply of fresh water for the establishment ('40 gallons per diem for each patient' being the recommendation of the Commissioners in Lunacy): this, and the building of a brewery on-site, together with the appointment of a master brewer for the provision of 'small beer' for the institution, was essential for the health of the patients and staff, for sanitation throughout the County was still somewhat rudimentary.

Most houses in Stratford-upon-Avon before 1850 had no house drainage and water closets were few. Excrement and the like was collected in cesspits, re-cycled by mixing with lime as 'nightsoil', and used as a fertiliser on the land.

Water came from pumps or from rain collected in waterbutts. In 1849, much of Coventry had no sewers at all, and those which did exist opened directly into the river Sherbourne. However, by the following year sewerage works for Coventry were completed: the average was one privy to six houses – but the sewage still discharged into the river Sherbourne; indeed, in 1870 the river was described as 'a large, open and extremely offensive sewer'. The Sherbourne sewage would eventually enter the river Avon – from which the town of Warwick obtained its drinking water. Cholera epidemics were frequent.

Sites for asylums had to have a pleasant prospect, be close to a town for the provision of staff and supplies and easily accessible by carriage or railway, as the Hatton site was, being near the Turnpike Road (now the Birmingham Road) and near the Hatton railway station, and which also had the additional advantage of good access via the Grand Union Canal for the delivery of building materials, provisions and the like.

A pleasant prospect was essential, indeed, but no doubt it was still considered a prudent, if perhaps unspoken, requirement to find a site that was 'free from the neighbourhood of houses, for the cries and exclamations of the outrageous would reach a great way and ought not to disturb the neighbours', which had been the advice of George Semple, the architect of St Patrick's Hospital, Dublin, a hundred years earlier, in 1752.[6]

Very meticulous requirements for asylum design were demanded by the Commissioners in Lunacy before any plans could hope to be submitted for their consideration; and they were well able to restrain the architects in their proposals:

> *Although we have no wish to advocate the erection of unsightly buildings we think no unnecessary cost should be incurred for architectural decoration; especially as these asylums are erected for persons who, when in health, are accustomed to dwell in cottages.*[7]

Three architects who had previously had asylum plans approved by the Commissioners were invited to 'furnish a plan for an asylum of three hundred patients'. They were Mr James Harris, the Engineer at the Hanwell Asylum, who was an accomplished architect and had designed the Kingston Asylum in Jamaica, the Halifax Asylum in Nova Scotia and would later design the Hampshire County Lunatic Asylum at Knowle; Mr Henry Duesbury, the architect of the Derby Lunatic Asylum, and Mr D R Hill, architect of the Birmingham Lunatic Asylum.

By December, the Committee had met and considered plans from the above three architects: three advisers had also been asked to 'assist the Committee in selection of a Plan for the Asylum'; one was Dr John Conolly, at that time Visiting Physician at Hanwell Asylum, and the other two were Mr Thomas Fulljames, County Surveyor for Gloucester and architect of North Wales Counties Lunatic Asylum at Denbigh and the Joint Counties Lunatic asylum at Abergavenny, and Dr Samuel Gaskell, then Medical Superintendent of the County Lunatic Asylum at Lancaster.

On 10th March 1848, Mr Harris's plan – a corridor design with capability of extension – had been chosen and costed at £45,829 15s 10d., excluding architect's commission, gas works, farm buildings and residence for a Chaplain (presumably eventually considered unnecessary, for only visiting Chaplains were ever appointed). This amounted to a capital cost of about £150 per patient: the Committee must have been pleased with these building costs, for it noted that it had before it 'the cost of 13 lunatic asylums already built, the average of which taken together was £162 per patient (the highest being £237 and the lowest £105)'.[8]

The Harris plans and costings were approved by the Committee, the Court of Quarter Sessions, the Commissioners in Lunacy and the Secretary of State, (in compliance with the provisions of the 1845 Act of Parliament).

In June 1848, Mr Harris requested the purchase of a further portion of land 'to admit the asylum to be created upon a more level surface', which was agreed, and by September Mr William Henry Betts, 'a respectable brickmaker at Warwick', agreed terms of 29d/1000 'for making 5 millions of bricks upon the premises', a fine bed of brick earth having been found in the land purchased.

Improving heating and lighting of the wards had been an early reform of Conolly's at Hanwell. He suggested to Mr Harris that the plans should be modified to provide openings over the doors for warming and ventilating the bedrooms, instead of the proposed inlets for heated air at the lower parts of the rooms, and some improvements to the windows. These final modification was agreed in January 1849.

★

It was now time to go to tender: advertisements inviting tenders were placed in 'all the papers in which County advertisements are inserted, twice in "The Times", and twice in "The Builder".

On 25 May John Heritage, a builder from Warwick, was awarded the contract to build the asylum, and John Croft of Brompton, Middlesex, was appointed Clerk of Works; and so, after thirty four months of deliberation, building the asylum commenced in earnest.

The foundation stone of the asylum was laid on 16 July 1849. Very little is recorded regarding the progress of building the Asylum. It must have been uneventful, apart from one building modification: Bath stone from the quarry at Box, near Bath, was substituted for the proposed Guiting stone, from the Temple Guiting quarry, near Cheltenham which, for some reason, at that time was unobtainable.

An additional 500,000 bricks were deemed necessary in March 1850; Mr Betts provided these once again, but made at his own kilns in Warwick, at a cost of 28d./1000; (1d./1000 less than the asylum's original contract price).

In November 1850 advertisements for the positions of Medical Superintendent, Clerk & Steward and Matron to the new asylum were placed in 'The Times', the 'Lancet' and the 'Mid Counties Herald' newspaper.

The first substantive appointments to the Asylum were made, commencing 1 May 1851: the position of Medical Superintendent (at £300 p.a. & accommodation, fire, light and washing and feed for one horse) had attracted nineteen applicants, which had been reduced to a short list of four, and of these Dr Henry Parsey, then Medical Assistant at the Devon County Asylum, was successful.

The Medical Superintendent had overall clinical and administrative responsibility for the asylum. Dr Parsey was required to visit and assess medically each patient daily; the Matron was responsible for the day-to-day care of the female patients (the sexes were, of course, segregated in practically every aspect of their daily lives), and when he visited each female patient daily in the female wing, the Matron was also required to be in attendance.

The 1845 Lunacy Act laid down in great detail his job description:

1. That he see every patient at least once in each day, and shall give up the whole of his time to the duties of his office, and shall not attend to or engage in any professional or other business or employment, except that of the asylum.
2. That he shall be superintendent of the asylum, and shall have authority to recommend the hiring and discharge of all attendants and servants, and shall also generally have the control over the male attendants and servants, and the authority to suspend them, whenever he shall deem expedient.
3. That he shall have a similar control, in common with the matron, over the female attendants and servants, and authority to suspend them, whenever he shall deem expedient.
4. That he shall make a yearly report of the number of admissions, removals, and discharges during the year; and shall also, in conjunction, with the visiting physician (there was none at Hatton), make a like report as to the general condition of the patients, and such other matters as may appear expedient for the purpose of showing the state and management of the asylum.
5. That he shall be responsible for the condition of the patients, and shall confer from time to time with the visiting physician, as to individual cases, the patients

generally, their diet, and any other matters affecting the condition of the asylum.

6. That he shall be responsible for the management and condition of the establishment, and shall have the direction of the medical, surgical, and moral treatment of the patients, and of all general arrangements within the asylum.

7. That he shall examine every patient on admission, and make proper entries relevant thereto; and he shall see every patient at least once a day, and take care that such medicines as he may deem proper be duly administered.

8. That he shall classify the patients of both sexes; and shall regulate and determine at all times on the diet for sick and infirm patients; and also that he shall have the power, from time to time, of examining and reporting on the quality of all provisions furnished for the use of the patients.

9. That he shall never absent himself for one night or more without the previous written consent of one of the committee of visitors; and then only on condition of his providing a person properly qualified to reside in the asylum, and perform his duty during his absence.

10. That he shall superintend and direct the performances of the duties of the matron, attendants, and servants, as prescribed by the "Regulation and Orders" of the committee of visitors.

11. That he shall at all times, and more especially when the asylum is entirely or early full, promote the exchange of harmless chronic patients for patients whose cases may be recent and supposed to be curable, or who shall be reported as dangerous.

12. That he shall report to the committee of visitors, and also to the house committee, at every visit, the name of every patient fit for discharge, and also the case of every

inquest, death, and escape that shall have occurred since the last preceding visit.

13. That he shall keep a journal, in which he shall make the following entries, viz.: 1st, The name of every attendant and servant whom he shall suspend, together with the date and cause of such suspension; and 2nd, The name of every patient fit for discharge, or who shall have escaped since the last visit of the committee, and all other such facts, observations, and suggestions as he shall deem important, relative to the condition or management of the asylum or the patients therein. And such entries shall be read as part of the proceedings, at the next meetings of the house committee and the committee of visitors respectively.

The power of the Medical Superintendent within the asylum was very much absolute, and remained so well into the 20th Century: Dr Francis Pilkington, who had been Deputy Physician Superintendent at the Warwick asylum in 1945 (then known as 'Warwick County Mental Hospital') discovered on his appointment in 1946 as Physician Superintendent to Moorhaven Hospital, Devon, (an asylum built in 1892), to his consternation, that no member of the nursing staff could marry without his express permission.[9] This stipulation he immediately rescinded.

Also from 1 May were appointed Eliza Turkington, of Wisbech, as Matron (£60 & accommodation, fire, light and washing) and Margaret Hurst, to be her servant, (at £7 p.a.).

Philomon Price Sanders, of Warwick, was appointed Clerk & Steward to the Asylum (at £100 p.a. & accommodation, light, fire and washing).

He too was, under statute, to:

1. Take care of all the books and papers (except the medical

books); and shall be responsible for the quantity, quality, and safe keeping of all articles received.

2. That he shall superintend the stores and all the weighing and measuring of the provisions, so as to suit the diet tables.

3. That he shall take stock once a quarter, and keep quarterly accounts of all monies received and paid to the treasurer; and also of all goods ordered and payments made for the same, in such form as the committee of visitors shall direct.

4. That he shall distinguish the building account from the maintenance account, and the accounts of the county from those of the unions and parishes; and shall lay an abstract of the accounts before the visitors at the quarterly meetings, showing the monies received and paid, and the unions and parishes in arrear.

He was to remain in post at the asylum until he retired, for reasons of ill health, in 1870. Amongst Henry Parsey's papers is a single brief handwritten note:

With the kind regards of Mr & Mrs Sanders and family as a small acknowledgement of the great kindness and attention shewn to them by Dr & Mrs Parsey in times of illness and anxiety.

Hatton
September 30th 1870

Dr Parsey must have had many similar letters from patients' relatives and staff of the asylum during his career, (indeed, in his diary he records being given 'a handsome small clock for supposed special services rendered') and it surprising that only this single 'thank you note' has been preserved. It must have been written on the occasion of Mr Sanders' retirement, and presumably had special significance and sentimental value for Henry Parsey, for Philomon Price Sanders and he had been appointed together, and plainly they had an excellent personal relationship. Whatever item accompanied the note regrettably must remain a mystery.

★

The day-to-day running of the Asylum in all its complexity, would, in time, come to include the Asylum's adjoining farms, the laundry, brewery, water supply and reservoir and the Asylum's own fire service (manned by the male attendants and some of the more *compos mentis* of the patients), and be the responsibility, for the main part, of the Clerk & Steward.

The appointment of the Asylum's first visiting Chaplain, Rev Charles Woods, a graduate of TCD and the Curate of Budbrook, (at £60 p.a.) was made on 10 June and the Engineer, Harry Flowers, was appointed on 1 July at one guinea (£1.05p) p.a.[10] It is interesting that the Committee should have decided to apply a professional man's fee structure for solely the engineer's remuneration.

How did these salaries compare to remuneration in other institutions? It is difficult to make strict comparisons, but from the Salaries and Wages ledger in the Asylum archive, in 1899 the then Medical Superintendent, Dr Alfred Miller, was receiving a salary of £800 p.a. which included a furnished house, coal, gas, vegetables and feed for one horse (still an essential requirement for travel, of course).

In comparison, in 1899 Professor Alfred Mettam, Professor of Anatomy at the Royal Veterinary School, in Edinburgh, was appointed the first Principal of the Royal Veterinary College of Ireland at a salary of £400 p.a., with the promise of a dwelling house on site (the new College had yet to be built). It is not revealed if Professor Mettam was entitled to feed for one horse or not.

THE GROUNDS OF THE ASYLUM

With moral management came the realisation that a tranquil environment – both internal and external – was conducive to mental recovery. Daniel Tuke, grandson of William Tuke, wrote in his 'Description of the Retreat', published in 1813, of the necessity of using the landscape as a therapeutic tool, by providing visual interest for the patients and also offering 'useful labour' within the grounds, the physical exercise relieving the tedium of daily life and also being of some economic benefit to the institution.

Statute determined that asylums built after 1845 had to have extensive grounds, which were modeled on the estates of large country houses and the new commercial cemeteries, such as Highgate, which were also designed to be 'pleasure gardens' for visitors. Not only did the Commissioners in Lunacy have stringent rules regarding asylum sites and designs, but they also stipulated the size and basic design for an asylum's grounds:

> *The airing courts, pleasure grounds, gardens, and fields annexed to an asylum, should be of such an extent as to afford the patients ample means of exercise and recreation, as well as of healthful employment out of doors: and should, as far as possible, be in the ratio of at least one acre to ten patients.*[11]

The inference was that a pleasant prospect and the practical occupation of plant cultivation and general gardening, would elevate mood and thus 'sooth the savage breast'. So it was a logical decision for the Committee to engage a professional horticulturalist as the designer of the grounds of the new asylum. Their choice was Richard Ashwell, the Superintendent of the London Road Cemetery, Coventry.

Richard Ashwell, had been apprenticed at the age of sixteen to Joseph Paxton, then the Head Gardener at Chatsworth, in Derbyshire. In 1845 Paxton had been approached by Coventry Corporation to landscape a new cemetery for the City, on the London Road, on land which was a disused quarry. It would be one of the first purpose-built cemeteries financed by a local authority: earlier purpose-built cemeteries such as Highgate and Key Hill, Birmingham, had been commercial enterprises, established to provide dignified disposal of the dead, for many churchyards had become seriously overcrowded – and some were becoming something of a public health concern. (Over 60,000 persons had been buried in the churchyard of St Philip's Cathedral in Birmingham between its consecration in 1715 and closure for burial in 1858, because it was becoming 'offensive to the surrounding neighborhood, especially in the summer months').

So, in early 1846, with two assistants, his son-in-law G H Stokes and Richard Ashwell, now married and with a young family, Paxton set about designing the cemetery. It was to have an imposing Italianate entrance lodge, an Anglican chapel in the Norman style, and a Non-conformist chapel in the Classical style, within a picturesque parkland of wooded walks framed by mature elms and a wide range of exotic forest trees and terraces for quiet contemplation. The northern area has no graves, being solely a 'pleasure ground' for visitors.

The cemetery opened on 19 December 1847 with Richard Ashwell as its first Superintendent, who lived in the gatehouse with his family for many years. He supervised many additional features that were added to the landscape by way of monuments and family tombs, and continued the planting of shrubs and specimen trees.

It remains one of the most elegant Victorian cemeteries of the 1840s, with the continued survival within the grounds of many of the original specimen trees, perhaps now grown to be a trifle overwhelming to the original landscape design. This and the cemetery at Witton, Birmingham, are now the only extant examples of his landscaping and planting capabilities.

For the asylum, his remit was to determine the site of the Gatehouse, from which he designed a sweeping approach road to the central tower of the main entrance – a common landscape design for asylums, hence the expression 'going round the bend' – and to lay out the airing courts, with ha-has, on the advice of Henry Parsey, allowing uninterrupted views of the parkland which he also laid out, which also included a farm, a four acre kitchen garden and a half-acre burial ground.[12]

By 1857 the grounds had undergone 'much improvement both useful and ornamental', but there is no surviving formal record in the Asylum archive of the specimen trees and other woody plants in the parkland. Curiously, no full-time head gardener was employed: the care of the grounds were the responsibility of the farm 'bailiff & gardener'. It all sounds just a touch utilitarian in design and expenditure.

In the fullness of time, Richard Ashwell's landscaping of the asylum's grounds matured, according to a description of a visit made to the asylum published in the 'Royal Leamington Spa Courier' of 9 February 1889:

A brisk, half-hour's walk from the county town, along the Birmingham Road, brings the visitor to the gates of the Asylum, which, as one would anticipate, is surrounded by a wall, though scarcely of sufficient height to prove an effectual barrier to the further progress of such patients as may be prompted, by a love of travel, to explore the regions outside. The summons for admission is promptly attended to, the side gate is opened, and the visitor quickly finds himself in the spacious grounds, in the middle of which the asylum stands. It is only now that he discovers the full extent of and nature of these grounds, forming, as they do, a complete little park, intersected by a broad carriage drive and well-kept gravel walks, thick shrubberies fringing the lawn-like plots of grass, while the buildings themselves are partially hidden by the tall trees that grow around. The drive leads directly to the main entrance of the asylum, and, upon ascending the short flight of steps here, a splendid view of the countryside around, on three sides, is obtained.

All that remains today are some of the parkland trees and a number of now somewhat overgrown Lawson's cypress trees (*Chamaecyparis lawsonii*) framing the main entrance, although a solitary cedar of Lebanon (*Cedrus libani*) in the lawn just to the right of the entrance is now splendidly majestic in its maturity (although not so majestic as 'Capability' Brown's signature cedar – albeit one hundred years older – similarly sited on the lawn at Compton Verney, a country house some eleven miles to the south of the county).[13]

Unfortunately, many key elements of topography of the grounds have been obliterated beneath the present housing estate, except for an area of ground to the east of the asylum which has been left as parkland, and which had been the burial ground for the asylum.

Although a Register of Deaths in the Asylum from 1852–1891 survives, in which the register number, name, abode, date of birth and age at death of the person concerned – whose burial was almost invariably conducted by the Chaplain to the asylum or on rare occasions by his curate or on very rare occasions indeed by members of the clergy of other parishes – is dutifully recorded, the plans of the first burial ground show only the first and last grave of each row of the 582 patients who are interred in the peculiarly-shaped burial ground.

Not only that, but a second layer of graves was dug, at a shallower level, so that the burial ground received a total of 1990 of the deceased of the asylum, before the second burial ground opened in January 1891.[14]

Appalling to present day sensibilities, perhaps, but it was common practice at the time for those patients who had died in asylums and been abandoned by their families to be interred in anonymous burial grounds in an area of the grounds remote from the overall grand design of the asylum's 'pleasure gardens'.

The asylum opened to receive its first patients on 29 June 1852. On 11 January 1853, Dr Acland, Physician to the Radcliffe Infirmary, Oxford, received a letter in which the correspondent remarked 'Mr Harris, the Hanwell engineer, was the architect of the Warwick and Hampshire asylums, which are the best in England'.[15]

ENDNOTES

1. Langley *Warwick County Asylum*
2. ibid.
3. In 1842 there were 406 lunatics in the county, but only 60 in private licensed 'madhouses'; the remainder were being accommodated in their homes.
4. Allegations by John Perceval of false confinement and mistreatment while an inmate of Brislington House helped to stimulate the formation of 'The Alleged Lunatic's Friend Society'.
5. Possible sites had included Norton Lindsay, Lillington, Barford, Upper Norton and Old Stratford.

6. St Patrick's Hospital was founded in 1746 with a legacy from Dr Jonathan Swift, DD, Dean of St Patrick's Cathedral, who had died in 1745. It opened to receive its first patients in 1757.
7. Report of Commissioners in Lunacy, 1844.
8. Rutherford *Landscapes for the Mind.*
9. Obituary Dr Francis Pilkington *Psych Bulletin* 1992, 16:377-8.
10. He remained in post until his retirement in 1880.
11. Report of Commissioners in Lunacy, 1847.
12. Rutherford *Landscapes for the Mind.*
13. Compton Verney; seat of the Verney family until 1921. The house was remodelled in 1762 by Robert Adam, with landscaping by 'Capability' Brown in 1769.
14. The youngest burial was that of Robert Aris, aged 5 years (one of a number of pre-teen burials of, presumably, idiots), and the eldest burial was that of Zephaniah Hands, a woman aged 90 years.
15. The Hampshire County Asylum had opened in December 1852. Russian prisoners of war from the Crimea had assisted in its construction; whether this was also true of the Hatton Asylum is not known.

CHAPTER 3

HENRY PARSEY'S TEACHERS:
DR JOHN CONOLLY & DR JOHN BUCKNILL

On accepting the position of President of the Medico-Psychological Association in 1876, Henry Parsey remarked:

> *It was my good fortune to be a recipient of Dr Conolly's earnest and eloquent instruction in his clinical teaching at Hanwell; instruction, that it was in my power to mature by associating myself, a few years later, at the Devon Asylum in its earliest days with Dr John Bucknill.*

Who were these two doctors, and why were they so influential on him? In fact, Conolly and Bucknill were two of the foremost alienists of the age. Dr John Conolly, who had previously been in medical practice in Stratford-upon-Avon and Warwick, was then the Resident Physician (equivalent to Medical Superintendent) at the Middlesex Asylum, Hanwell, when, in the summer of 1842, he gave a course of six clinical lectures on insanity to selected medical students from London medical schools – amongst whom was Henry Parsey.

Dr (later Sir) John Bucknill was the Medical Superintendent at the Devon County Lunatic Asylum, at Exminster, when, after qualification, Henry Parsey became his Assistant Medical Officer for five years, until he was appointed the Medical Superintendent at Hatton.

DR JOHN CONOLLY

John Conolly was born on 27 May 1794 in Market Rasen, in Lincolnshire. His father came from 'an obscure branch' of the Irish Conolly family, of which the most illustrious member was William, Speaker of the Irish House of Commons from 1715-1729, who was always referred to as 'Speaker Conolly' and who had built in 1724 what is considered to be the finest Palladian house in Ireland, Castletown House, in Celbridge, Co. Kildare – Conolly's daughter Sophia (b 1822), allegedly recalled holidays spent there as a child.[1]

John's father died when he was young and his mother remarried a Scot who had lived in Paris, who taught John and his elder brother fluency in French, which was to prove useful to them both in later years.

After schooling, he joined the Cambridgeshire Militia as an ensign. In 1817, after three years with the militia, he left and married Elizabeth Collins, the daughter of a naval captain, and went to live for a year in a cottage near Tours, where his elder brother William, who had qualified MRCS in 1814, was in practice as a surgeon. (William was to return to England in 1835 and open a private asylum in Charlton Kings, near Cheltenham, which he named 'Castletown House').

After passing 'the happiest year of his life' in Tours, and now with a daughter, Eliza (b 1818), he had to think seriously of adopting some profession or other regular means of livelihood. He decided upon medicine, and enrolled at Edinburgh University.

Edinburgh may be the 'Athens of the North', but for Conolly it was 'a great and dreary change' from Tours, with which one can sympathise.[2] Be that as it may, he appears to have applied himself diligently to his studies, was noted to be 'of amiable disposition and courteous manners' – this was to stand him in good stead in future years – and became a president of the Royal Medical Society (an Edinburgh medical student society).

On 1 August 1821, on completion of his studies and successfully defending his dissertation to the satisfaction of the examiners, the University conferred the degree of MD – Doctor of Medicine – on him (and one hundred and one other gentlemen).

Conolly's dissertation was entitled *'De statu mentis in insania et melancholia'* ['An Inquiry Concerning the Mental Conditions of Insanity and Depressive Illness'] – an early indication of his interest in the subject of mental health, perhaps.

Like many another young doctor, with only his skills to support him, he immediately entered general medical practice, initially in Lewes, in Sussex, then in Chichester. A colleague and friend Dr John Forbes, (also an Edinburgh graduate, although not a contemporary), was a physician to the Chichester Infirmary. Perhaps there was an uncomfortable sense of competition, because, after a visit to various medical institutions in Paris (including the Bicêtre and Salpetrière Hospitals), he moved the family, which now also included a son, Edward (b 1822), to Stratford-upon-Avon, in Warwickshire.

★

A notice appeared on page 3 of the 'Warwick Advertiser' on 29 March 1823:

Dr Conolly, former President of the Royal Medical Society of Edinburgh and late one of the physicians to the Chichester Public Dispensary, author of 'Observations on Vaccines etc' has become resident physician at Stratford-upon-Avon.

He was of 'amiable disposition and courteous manners', as we know, and his practice in the town appears to have flourished: he expanded his 1822 pamphlet on vaccination, originally written in Chichester, into a book entitled "Observations on Vaccination, and on the Practice of Inoculating for the Smallpox", by John Conolly MD Physician to the Stratford Dispensary etc. and published this in Stratford in 1824.[3] It was apparently well received, and no doubt assisted in raising his professional profile in the town.

It was decided at a meeting in Stratford Town Hall in August 1823 to create a Dispensary. Subscribers could nominate suitable patients for admission, and financial support would come from public appeals including an annual pre-Christmas sale and a fund-raising Dispensary Ball in the Town Hall, which became something of a highpoint in Stratford's social calendar.

The Dispensary, a surgery and two small wards, was established in the Old Bank Building in Chapel Street, and opened in September 1823, under the day-to-day supervision of a matron. 'Gratuitous services' offered by two Stratford surgeons and Conolly were accepted, with Conolly providing annual printed medical reports of the workings of the Dispensary to the Governors and Subscribers at their Annual General Meeting in the Town Hall.

In its first year of opening, three hundred and thirty patients were treated in the Dispensary.[4] It appears to have run uneventfully in its early years, for the 1826 AGM minuted that 'the thanks of the meeting be given to Dr

Conolly for his valuable attention to and supervision of the benevolent intention of the institution.'

He was also involved in establishing the Dispensary in Warwick, housed in a fine stone building (which up until only recently continued to house a medical practice), which opened in 1826, and was likewise funded by public subscription and an annual charity ball.

Pressure on beds in Stratford must have been great during the early years of its operation, and understandably the Dispensary moved to bigger premises in Chapel Lane in 1839, and renamed itself Stratford-upon-Avon Infirmary.[5] In 1884, it, in turn, was replaced by a new hospital on Arden Street, in 1884, built on land in front of the 1836 Workhouse.[6]

Conolly's house in Stratford in Henley Street, now demolished, was adjacent to Shakespeare's Birthplace. In 1824 Conolly became a founding member of the Stratford-upon-Avon Shakespeare Club, the oldest Shakespearean Society in existence. The Shakespeare Club was responsible for acquiring Shakespeare's birthplace and the formation of the Shakespeare Birthplace Trust, and also the preservation of Shakespeare's grave and memorial in Holy Trinity Church.[7]

Conolly had always had a great affection for Shakespeare (as had Henry Parsey's other teacher John Bucknill), and remained a member of the Club until 1846; it is said when he was visiting patients on his rounds in practice he used to carry a copy of Shakespeare's sonnets in his coat pocket.

Indeed Conolly's last published work in 1863 was an analysis of Hamlet's psychological state: was he, or was he not, mad? He concluded 'it was Shakespeare's intention to represent Hamlet as completely relapsed into distraction'.[8] (John Bucknill's opinion was contrary: he thought that Hamlet's madness was feigned).

Conolly had been elected to the Town Council in June 1823, three months after his arrival in the town, became an alderman in March 1825, (remaining an alderman until he moved to Hanwell in 1839), and served as Mayor from 7 September 1825 to 6 September 1826. He was obviously working very hard indeed to integrate himself into the local community.

In 1823 he had also been appointed 'Inspecting Physician to the lunatic houses for the County of Warwickshire', his duties being to visit each licensed 'mad-house' in the county annually, (of which there were three at the time; two in Henley-in-Arden, containing forty one and sixteen lunatics respectively, and one in Wooten Wawen, containing three), accompanied by two Justices of the Peace.

The visits were somewhat cursory, the object being, in essence, (under the 1774 Act for Regulating Madhouses), to ensure that no inmates were being detained illegally, rather than an inspection regarding standards of care and provision of creature comforts for the inmates of the houses. Conolly found the visits decidedly superficial in content:

> *when official visits were made, all presented their best appearance, but the general spectacle was distressing…noise and affront combined to disturb and affright the visitors, who were glad to retreat from a scene they deplored and considered unavoidable. Patients too furious to be congregated were locked in their rooms, into which few visitors ventured even to look.*[9]

It is doubtful he would have found this duty particularly rewarding, even given his interest in the treatment of the insane, but a fee is a fee, and for all his charm and popularity, his income during his Stratford years was never very great.

He was, therefore, probably relieved to be able to relinquish the post in 1828 when he was approached to become the first 'Professor of the Nature and Treatment of Diseases' in the medical school at University College, of the new University of London.

When this became known in the town, a dinner was arranged in his honour by Sir Gray Skipwith,[10] Chairman of the Dispensary Committee and Recorder of Stratford-upon-Avon, which was attended by over two hundred townspeople, who plainly held him in high regard.

Sir Gray spoke of Conolly as 'a skillful and benevolent physician, and an indefatigable friend to the poor and afflicted', and presented him with a silver salver inscribed:

> *To John Conolly M.D.*
> *from the inhabitants of Stratford-upon-Avon*
> *and its neighbourhood,*
> *as a testimony of their esteem and regard.*
> *Sept 18th 1828*

So the family, which now included a second daughter, Sophia (b 1826), moved to London.

Regrettably, his sojourn in London turned out to be brief, despite his becoming a Licentiate (by examination) of the Royal College of Physicians the following year: he held his Professorial post for just over two years, before resigning in December 1830.

The reasons for his resignation were complex. The new University expected staff members of the medical school to supplement their – somewhat parsimonious – incomes by private practice (although securing a decent clientele of patients, as a newly established London physician, from the highly competitive 'carriage trade' was probably no easy matter); whereas Conolly considered his time could be better spent lecturing and in research, as an academic physician – on a decent income. And although he wrote a textbook on insanity during this time, his attempts to introduce lectures to the students on insanity as part of the undergraduate course were thwarted.[11] That innovation would have to wait until his appointment to the Hanwell Asylum in 1842. It would be well into the 1860s, in fact, before there were formal lectures on insanity in the curriculum of the University's medical school.

There was more to it than that, though. The new University had as yet no Hospital – University College Hospital (UCH) did not open until 1834 – and in the interim medical students received very much a theoretical training only. Conolly instituted a small dispensary and an outpatient clinic in George Street, north of Euston Road, thus allowing the students some contact with clinical medical practice, but had a clash of personality with the resident apothecary, John Hogg, with whom he had, allegedly, bitter quarrels.

In the event it was Conolly who offered his resignation, plainly with some regret, it appears, for he wrote to the Council:

I had no prospect of succeeding in a noble design [academic medicine] to which I would gladly have devoted my mind, and my time, and even my life.[12]

However, harbouring ill-feeling probably was not in Conolly's nature, for his relations with University College appear to have remained cordial in subsequent years. For example, he received a request from University College, in 1847, to allow UCH medical students to 'walk the wards' and attend his instruction at Hanwell asylum, to which he replied:

It would of course gratify me to show in any way the particular interest I take in anything related to the Medical School of University College.[13]

★

But there were pressing matters to attend to: once again, he had no income and he discovered his practice in Stratford-upon-Avon had been taken over – rather successfully apparently – by a Dr John Staunton, who was also the new 'Inspecting Physician of lunatic houses.'

He was now aged 36, with a wife and four young children, for his youngest daughter, Ann Caroline, had been born in 1830, whilst they were in London. Conolly was practically in the same position financially as he had been when he left Edinburgh and had had to 'put up his plate' as a general practitioner.

This time it was to Warwick, where he had been involved in opening the town's Dispensary some years earlier, that he and his family removed. They were to stay in Warwick for the next seven years, first settling in Swan Street. For some unknown reason, it was not until February 1832 that Ann, who had been born in London, came to be baptized in St Mary's Church, Warwick. The family moved to Theatre Street in 1833, then to a house in the High Street in 1835 and finally to a house in New Road in 1839.

Once again, Conolly became very active within local medical and social circles. He continued as an alderman of Stratford Town Council, and a member of the Shakespeare Club in Stratford; he helped to found the Provincial Medical and Surgical Association (which eventually became the British Medical Association) with Dr (later Sir) Charles Hastings of Worcester and Dr (also later Sir) John Forbes, his erstwhile colleague in Chichester,[14] and with his elder brother William, now returned from France and the proprietor of 'Castletown House',[15] acting as Treasurer & Secretary.

Conolly appears to have had a flair for organization

and persuasion: soon after his arrival in Warwick he had been instrumental in forming, and becoming President of, the 'Warwick and Leamington Phrenology Society', in 1834. Among the founder members were John Bucknill, surgeon, of Rugby, (father to John Bucknill of the Devon County Asylum), and Dr Henry Lilley Smith, surgeon, of Southam,[16] who had opened in that town the first provident (self-supporting) dispensary in England, for the treatment of diseases of the eye.

Phrenology was the art of diagnosing a person's character and psychological strengths and weaknesses by palpation of the exterior of the skull, and had rapidly become a fashionable medical diagnostic technique following its introduction from Germany in the early 1800s; however, it was soon considered to be a valueless procedure, and was totally discarded by orthodox physicians by the middle of the Century.

Presumably the technique's fall from grace was why Conolly proposed forming a new society, 'which would embrace the several departments of Natural History', to an assembled company of interested persons in the Court House on 12 April 1836, offering to transfer subscriptions, books, casts and other property of the Phrenology Society to the new Society.

This proposal was well received, and thus the 'Warwick Natural History and Archaeological Society' was born, with the Earl of Warwick as Patron and Conolly as the new Hon. Sec. One month later the Society obtained 'one of the large rooms in the Market Hall for the immediate reception of specimens for the Museum, with a prospect of obtaining another of equal size and equally well lighted, together with rooms for a Curator, at a reasonable rent'.

The new Society thrived, accepting many donations of natural history specimens, such that it soon occupied the whole of the first floor of the Market Hall (and continues to do so today as part of the Warwickshire Museum), and over seven hundred members and friends attended the first quarterly meeting in the National School in Chapel Street.

Among those who joined in the early years were the Rev Dr Thomas Arnold, Headmaster of Rugby School (of 'Tom Brown's Schooldays' fame)[12], Dr Henry Jephson, a fashionable physician practicing in Leamington Priors (as Leamington Spa was then known), and who had been instrumental in developing the town as a spa (and accumulating much personal wealth in so doing), who later became a Committee member, and one Dr Henry Parsey, who joined following his appointment to Hatton, and became a Committee member in 1866.

After forming the Natural History Society, Conolly did not rest on his laurels, for he, a Dr Loudon, and 'several other gentlemen, resident in or near Leamington', founded a 'Mechanics Institute' in Leamington, also in 1836. Initially the Institute held meetings in the Parragon Rooms in the High Street, but were later able to secure rooms in Bath Street, and there assembled a library of over two hundred volumes, including many valuable donations.[18]

It seems Conolly did not have such a busy clinical practice (if any) in Warwick, compared to his Stratford years, and he seems to have made a living for the family just by his literary work and from editing the 'British and Foreign Medical Review' with Dr John Forbes, his fluency in French allowing him to make reports for the journal on medical advances on the Continent.

He was much involved with giving and arranging lectures and attending field trips on natural history topics for the Warwick Natural History Society, and he also spent some months in 1838 lecturing at the new medical school in Birmingham (whose students qualified by taking the Society of Apothecaries examination in London), with another Edinburgh contemporary, Dr John Darnall, who was by then established as a paediatrician in Birmingham. He also visited Dr Robert Gardiner Hill at the Lincoln Lunatic Asylum, the first physician to an asylum in England to have totally abolished mechanical restraint. This visit influenced Conolly greatly, and would prove to be a turning point in improving the treatment of the insane in England.

This somewhat financially precarious existence was to end in 1839, when – to the consternation of his medical friends, who considered he was committing professional suicide – he was appointed Resident Physician at the Middlesex County Asylum at Hanwell, then the largest asylum in England.

Once again, farewell dinners were held in his honour on his leaving Warwickshire for the second time; firstly, by his co-editor Dr John Forbes, and secondly, by the other members of the Shakespeare Club, who wanted to recognize his work for the Society by arranging yet another dinner in Stratford's Town Hall. It was said during the evening that:

> *Dr Conolly had received an appointment in every way suitable to his wishes, and which might, indeed, be looked upon as a fitting reward for his talents, and a public recognition of these merits which had so long and so highly been estimated by his friends.*
>
> *The Magistracy of Middlesex had conferred great honour upon themselves in selecting a gentleman who had devoted during a long series of years, so much attention to that particular branch of medical science, and was, in every way, eminently qualified to protect and relieve the unfortunate individuals whose distressing maladies might place them under his care.*

His friends may have considered his decision to move to Hanwell was professional suicide, but the Town evidently considered he was taking up a post of high esteem.

★

And so the family moved to London once again, Conolly taking up his post in June 1839.

Within three months of his appointment at Hanwell, he had followed Gardiner Hill by also totally abolishing mechanical restraint in the asylum, reporting to the Governors in his first Annual Report of 22 September, 1839, that 'in an asylum of over 800 patients, there were now none restrained by strait-jacket, leg locks, straps or coercion chair', (thus requiring the asylum to dispose of 49 restraining chairs, 78 restraining sleeves, 352 leg-locks and handcuffs, 51 long leather straps, 10 leather muffs, two extra-strong iron chain leg-locks and two screw-gags).[19] It was an astonishing achievement, especially by a physician with no practical experience of running an asylum of any size at all.

Because non-restraint improved the behaviour of the inmates of the asylum – 'when the patient is tied up, all regard for him ceases' – a more tranquil climate pervaded the asylum, and Conolly found it possible to commence clinical instruction to medical students because 'scenes of general confusion and agitation had become rare [...] and the actual state of the minds of the insane was in most cases displayed to the learner.'[20]

In the summer of 1842, Conolly delivered a course of lectures on six consecutive Saturdays at Hanwell to ten medical students, on various aspects of lunacy; each lecture was preceded by a visit to the wards in two groups, accompanied by the House Surgeon:

'The wards were tranquil, the patients were cheerful; and the visits of the pupils were looked forward to with interest.'[21]

Henry Parsey was among that group of ten students.

Conolly wrote in his Annual Report of 1843 to the Hanwell Visitors:

'the medical students selected to attend the lectures were gentlemen who had nearly, or entirely, completed their general medical studies. Their demeanour was such as to make their visits to the wards rather salutary, rather than in the smallest degree distressing, to the patients they saw and conversed with. A way has thus been prepared for a very important addition to Medical studies, the result of which will not be without value to the public.'

Diagnosis before treatment: the foundation stone of modern clinical practice. Conolly considered the Resident Physician should have ultimate responsibility of the asylum, but it seems increasing degrees of interference by the Governors in non-clinical matters – ever the curse of hospital clinicians – culminating in their reducing his responsibility to purely medical care of the inmates, led him to resign his post in 1844, and become 'Visiting Physician' (which he continued to be until 1852), by moving into a private residence, Lawn House, near the asylum.

On finally severing all professional connection with the asylum in 1852, he was presented with a very large silver 'testimonial', nearly a metre in height: it had a figure of Aesculapius, the God of healing, at the apex, flanked by figures personifying Mercy and Science. Below are figures derived from 'Raving' and 'Melancholy Madness', [Bedlam's 'brainless brothers'], a female patient convalescing, and a male patient being restored to his welcoming family, and gratefully pointing up to the agents of his recovery. At the base are plaques presenting life in the asylum before and after non-restraint. Before, the patients are locked in a dungeon, their heads shaved for bleeding; after, they make themselves useful in a fruitful garden, grasping the hand of their physician.[22]

The inscription reads:

This Testimonial
Of His
Strenuous Persevering
And
SUCCESSFUL LABOURS
To Improve The Treatment
And
Ameliorate The Condition
OF THE INSANE
Is
Together With A Portrait Of Himself
Presented
By His
Admiring And Grateful
Cotemporaries [sic]
To
JOHN CONOLLY M.D.
Physician
To The Hanwell Lunatic Asylum
AD MDCCCLII

In the same year Oxford University awarded him an honorary Doctorate in Civil Law.

Conolly then opened Lawn House for the reception of six (wealthy) female lunatics, and continued to do so until his death: with much irony, the wheel had appeared to have turned full circle, for here he was, a proprietor of a private 'mad-house', which he had condemned for most of his professional life as being totally unsuited to the restoration of sanity. Such is life.

He also acted occasionally as an expert witness, and in 1857 wrote what became the standard text on asylum design and care 'On The Construction and Development of Lunatic Asylums and other Hospitals for the Insane'.

In his later years, his definitions of insanity in his writings came to include the merely obnoxious features of human behaviour, which were entitled 'moral insanity'; even in the 1850s causes of insanity included 'monotony of toil', 'misery & anxiety' and 'beer & gin' in the lower classes; 'stress of business', 'excessive competition' and 'reckless & intemperate living' in the middle classes and 'intemperance', 'multiplicity of objects of study in youth', 'luxurious habits' and 'desultory life' among the upper classes.[23] It is easy, therefore, to see how the diagnosis of insanity would lead eventually to the confinement of the merely wilful, the tiresome and the unruly – although, surprisingly, this was to be very much more an early 20th Century phenomenon than ever it was in the nineteenth Century.

However, Conolly returned in 1863 to Shakespeare and his pamphlet 'A Study of Hamlet', referred to earlier, for his final writings. He was to die of a stroke in Lawn House in 1866, and was buried in Kensington Cemetery, Ealing.

A few months before his death, his daughter Ann had married Dr Henry Maudsley,[24] the Professor of Medical Jurisprudence at University College, who took over the running of Lawn House, and its occupants, until 1874.

Later, in the same year as his death, a marble bust of Conolly by the Italian sculptor Cavalieri Benzoni was presented to the Medico-Psychological Association at their annual meeting in Edinburgh. At that time, the Association had no permanent home, so it was offered to the Royal College of Physicians, who, on moving to Regent's Park in 1966, displayed the bust in the entrance hall of their new building.

In 1988 a bronze copy of the bust was made for the Royal College of Physicians and the original was returned – reluctantly – to the Royal College of Psychiatrists, (the new title of the Medico-Psychological Association), which had finally acquired premises in Belgrave Square, London, where it is now on display in the boardroom.

DR JOHN BUCKNILL

If John Conolly's lectures to medical students had instilled in Henry Parsey a vocation for a career in lunacy, then it was John Bucknill, at the Exminster asylum who must have encouraged this desire during the five years that Henry Parsey was to be his Assistant Medical Officer.

Bucknill applied Conolly's regime of non-restraint during his ten years as Medical Superintendent at Exminster with considerable success, and was held in high regard professionally by his contemporaries in the field of lunacy.

He was the son of a surgeon, and was educated at Rugby School under Dr Arnold. Apparently he spent the first year of his medical training in Dublin, but at which institution is not known, before transferring to University College, London, from whence he graduated in 1840, four years before Henry Parsey, with gold medals in Anatomy and Materia Medica, and silver medals in Medicine and Surgery. He also qualified 'College and Hall' (MRCS & LSA) – the qualification required to be a 'surgeon-apothecary' (general practitioner) – in the same year; presumably as 'belt and braces', should he decide – Heaven forbid – to enter general practice at some point in the future (as Henry Parsey would also take in due course).

Shortly after a year as House Surgeon at UCH to Professor Robert Liston, a surgeon renowned for his speed of surgical amputation in the era before anaesthesia, John Bucknill's health became poor – possibly from tuberculosis – and he was advised to apply for a less taxing position, ideally in warmer climes.

In the event he was appointed Medical Superintendent of the new Devon County Lunatic Asylum, at the age of 27; another young physician appointed to the position of Medical Superintendent, despite a lack of any experience of the treatment of lunacy, yet he ran the asylum single-handedly from its opening in 1845 until Henry Parsey joined him as his Assistant Medical Officer in 1848.

Whilst Medical Superintendent of the asylum, Bucknill also introduced innovation into English care of the insane by boarding out some lunatics in houses in the town of Exminster itself. This, surprisingly, gained the approval of the Visitors to the Asylum, who reported that they 'would be glad if the example thus set were followed by the Visitors in other counties'.

In Scotland, such 'family care' for manageable lunatics was widely practiced; about a quarter of all certified lunatics, usually imbeciles or idiots, were boarded out, in ones and twos and at a fee, in private houses, which were regularly inspected by the Scottish Lunacy Board.[25] Many crofter families would therefore have had experience of caring for a lunatic within in the family, who most likely proved to be a useful additional pair of hands about the croft (also reducing prejudice against the insane one would like to think).

THE GHEEL COMMUNITY

The model for family care came originally from Gheel, a small town near Antwerp, in Belgium, which had been doing exactly this for many years, but the circumstances there were exceptional.

St Dymphna, a 7C. Irish saint and patron saint of the mentally disturbed, had died in Gheel; since the Renaissance the town had become a place of pilgrimage.

Gheel's citizens had therefore long experience of coping with an influx of large numbers of the insane; under medical supervision, the majority were boarded out with families, sometimes for considerable periods of time, and those lunatics who could would make themselves useful within the family circle; if any lunatics became dangerous or unmanageable, then they were confined in the town's (probably hard-pressed) asylum. It was the original model for 'care in the community'.

But 'family care' in England was much more unusual, despite the approval of the Devon asylum's Visitors: (no doubt it was argued that, after all, it helped to reduce overcrowding in the asylum, and in any case, were not asylums supposed to be for the care and cure of the insane, rather than merely accommodation for the incurable?).

Be that as it may, 'family care' did not gain wide acceptance in English asylums; many alienists considered that domiciliary care provided by unskilled carers often resulted in regressive behaviour of their charges, and, inevitably, re-admission to the asylum. The therapeutic effect of a bucolic idyll of 'thatched cottages, roses, bleating lambs and roaming goats', (as a visiting American journalist had described family care for the insane in Gheel in an article for his newspaper), was purely illusory. Besides, rumours from Scotland suggesting that boarded-out patients were often under-occupied, or even restrained if the family was otherwise too busy to manage them, and reports of some dwellings being primitive, cold, and often lacking sanitation just confirmed their doubts.

*

Bucknill was an enthusiastic member of the 'Association of Medical Officers of Asylums and Hospitals for the Insane' (AMOAHI), which had been formed in 1841; Conolly became its President for 1858, and Bucknill for 1860. Medical Superintendents were solitary creatures, for the main part, administering their asylums very much in isolation, and main aims of the Association were to improve communication between alienists and research best practice for the care of the insane.

Annual meetings were held at various venues and in Oxford in 1852 a learned journal was proposed and Bucknill was appointed editor. This first appeared as 'Asylum Journal', but it was renamed the 'Journal of Mental Science' in 1858, and then the 'British Journal of Psychiatry' from 1963 until the present day. Bucknill proved to be an enthusiastic editor and his son recalled that :

I used to ride my half-wild Exmoor pony backwards and forwards between Exminster Asylum and Pollard's, the printers, in Exeter, with proofs for the press. It mattered not what was the weather or the hour; I had to do it and do it quickly.[26]

He also co-authored in 1858 'A Manual of Psychological Medicine' with Daniel Hack Tuke, the great-grandson of William Tuke, of the York Retreat. This volume, which reads so very quaintly today, became the standard text on lunacy for the remainder of the nineteenth century.

The AMOAHI changed its name to the 'Medico-Psychological Association' at its annual meeting in Edinburgh in 1866 – this was the meeting at which the assembled members were presented with Benzoni's bust of John Conolly. Henry Parsey became its President in 1876-77. By this time the membership exceeded three hundred and sixty and included virtually all the Medical Superintendents (and some junior staff) of the asylums in England, Scotland and Ireland, a number of academic Professors of Medicine and Psychological Medicine and one of Midwifery,[27] and a number of overseas alienists, from asylums in Paris, Vienna, Newfoundland and Nova Scotia.

LORD CHANCELLOR'S VISITOR

After eighteen years at Exminster Dr Bucknill resigned his Superintendency and editorship of the Journal, on his appointment as one of the Lord Chancellor's two 'Visitors in Lunacy', the other Visitor being the well-regarded Dr William Hood, then Principal Physician of Bethlem Hospital.

'Persons of unsound mind and altogether unfit and too unable to govern themselves' and who had substantial property or income had their interests protected by the Lord Chancellor and the Court of Chancery (now the Court of Protection) from unscrupulous parties – often (but not always) other members of the family. The Court would review evidence submitted by two independent doctors and a request (usually from a near relative) for the Court's certification of the patient as incapable. If this 'inquisition' so agreed, two Masters in Lunacy, (judges appointed to the Court), would oversee the financial provision of care of the patients under its protection, the majority of whom were placed as single patients in private houses, although an increasing number were being accepted into the new pauper asylums, as 'private patients'. In 1862, there were about six hundred patients under the Court's protection (and nearly one thousand by the end of the century).

Each was visited at least twice a year by one of the two Visitors, whose duty was 'to ensure they had such comforts as their mental condition and income will allow of'; much more particular than John Conolly's duties when 'Inspecting Physician to the lunatic houses for the County of Warwickshire'. Like Conolly, who required the consent of two Justices to effect a discharge from a 'mad-house', a Visitor could not discharge a patient *per se*, but only recommend their discharge to the Court, if they considered any patient had recovered their wits sufficiently.

Each Visitor was paid £1500 per annum, and necessary expenses, and was prohibited from undertaking private practice.

This supervision sounds secure and robust enough, but there had always been some disquiet in the public eye that sane members of families were being inappropriately confined in private asylums, invariably so that their money or property – or both – could be misappropriated by other relatives.

The 'Alleged Lunatic's Friend Society' had been formed in 1845 by a number of persons who had been previously confined (wrongfully, they alleged) and who wished to amend the current legislation to give other alleged lunatics greater protection against wrongful committal and also offer legal advice.

Victorian 'sensation novels' whose plots revolved on unjust confinement of characters for monetary gain by relatives – of which the most popular were Wilkie Collins' 'The Woman in White', Charles Reade's 'Hard Cash' (which contains a scurrilous caricature of Conolly in the person of

Dr Wycherley, an asylum proprietor) and Charlotte Bronte's 'Jane Eyre' were – and remain – sensational reading, but they did nothing to allay the public's fears.

The British Medical Journal went so far as to suggest that:

> *Much might indeed be said in favour of the view that any alteration in the law that is to take place should tend to the opposite direction and remove some of the difficulties which it at present interposes in the way of putting a person of unsound mind into a place of safety.*[28]

Although concerns regarding wrongful confinement had been, rightly, of considerable concern to the public in the eighteenth century, they still would not go away: how widespread was such abuse of committal procedures at this time?

In 1877, Bucknill was appointed to a Select Committee 'to enquire into the operation of the Lunacy Law, regarding the security afforded by it against the violations of personal liberty'.

The Select Committee found little evidence of abuse, but that is not to say there was none at all. For example:

> *Mrs Catherine Linnett was a housekeeper to the Masters in Lunacy, late of 45 Lincoln's Inn Fields. Finding her ailing one morning, her husband asked Dr Bucknill to prescribe for her, which he did.*
>
> *Unfortunately, being ignorant of her constitution, he gave her morphia which instead of soothing her pains, excited her brain, and she became incoherent and delirious. Hereupon her husband called in two registered practitioners of the lower order, one keeping a shop in Clare Market. Even these objected at first to certifying, but Mr Linnett overcame their scruples, and Mrs Linnett was removed to Bethlehem. After some months, her husband consented to her return home, where she has led ever since a life of usefulness and perfect*

sanity, as she had done previously to Dr Bucknill's unfortunate mistake.[29]

The author of the above anecdote may have had her own axe to grind, but it was certainly a touch risky on Dr Bucknill's part to prescribe for Mrs Linnett in such circumstances; but her husband seems to have been very persuasive, certainly with regard to his successfully overcoming the scruples of the two doctors 'of the lower order' he had called in,[30] so perhaps Dr Bucknill had been overcome likewise; other physicians might well have behaved in a like manner. It is also regrettable that Mrs Linnett reacted in the way she did to the morphia injection, but paradoxical reactions (when pharmacological treatment has an effect opposite to that expected) do occur rarely and unpredictably, so perhaps he should not be censured too severely.

The 'Alleged Lunatic's Friend Society' did not survive for very long, ceasing to exist in about 1860; although it had successfully brought Bethlem Hospital under the inspection of the Commissioners in Lunacy (it had previously been exempt as a charitable institution), the Society never really receiving much public support.

LATER YEARS

After fourteen years as Lord Chancellor's Visitor Bucknill resigned, but continued to write on topics regarding lunacy from his house in Wimpole Street and occasionally acting as expert witness, although rarely indulging in any clinical practice.

Like Conolly, he too was an amateur Shakespearian scholar, and his 'graceful and powerful literary style' apparently suited essays he wrote on Shakespeare later in life. It is not known if he carried a copy of Shakespeare's sonnets in his coat pocket whilst he went on his daily rounds, as Conolly was wont to do during his years in Stratford, but one would like to think so.

'The Medical Knowledge of Shakespeare', published in 1860, reveals a close familiarity with Shakespeare's texts, and gives an erudite commentary on the medical observations made by many of the characters in the plays.

'The Mad Folk of Shakespeare' (psychological essays on King Lear, Macbeth, Lady Macbeth, Hamlet and Ophelia amongst others), published in 1867, makes very attractive reading too, perhaps because his analyses of the characters are rigorously supported in argument by confirmation from the text of each play. For example, he thought that Lady Macbeth was 'scarcely insane, but so sorely troubled in conscience as to be prone to quit the anguish of this life by means of suicide.' As happens.

And Hamlet's behaviour has 'the characteristics... of mania so mingled with native wit and disguised by the ground colour of real melancholy, shewing through the transparency of the feigned state [of madness], that Hamlet's character becomes one of the most interesting and complicated subjects of psychological study anywhere to be met with':[31] a diametrically opposite view to Conolly.

It is disappointing that this interest in Shakespeare, which was so evident in both his teachers, does not appear to have rubbed off on Henry Parsey to the slightest degree, as far as can be ascertained.

After his years as Visitor, Bucknill also spent much time in Warwickshire, living in the village of Hillmorton, near Rugby, and he became a Justice of the Peace and a Visitor of the Hatton asylum (thus renewing an acquaintance with his erstwhile assistant). He had married a Warwickshire girl in 1842, Maryanne Townsend, by whom he had three sons, and apparently indulged himself in the country pursuits of hunting, shooting and fishing, whilst residing at his wife's family farm at Hillmorton Hall. He was knighted in 1894.

After his wife died in 1889, he retired to Bournemouth, where he was to die on 20 July 1897, from 'septic inflammation from catheterism': in his last years he must have had to endure the rather taxing 'catheter life' because of an enlarged prostate gland which increasingly impairs the outflow of urine from the bladder. He has every sympathy.[32]

John Bucknill was buried on 22 July 1897, in a very fine tomb in the burial ground of St Mary's Church, Clifton-upon-Dunsmore, close to Hillmorton Hall. The tomb is rectangular in shape, with a yew tree planted at each corner; the trees are now becoming somewhat overpowering and dwarf the memorial, but the inscription on the tomb is still easily read:

> HERE LIETH THE REMAINS OF
> JOHN CHARLES BUCKNILL MD FRCP & JP
> KNIGHTED BY THE QUEEN IN 1895
> Late of Hillmorton Hall in this County
> BORN 25 DECEMBER 1817 DIED 19 JUNE 1897
> A FRIEND AND A PHYSICIAN OF THE INSANE

It is entirely understandable how these two formidable men, 'friends and physicians of the insane', perhaps would have influenced Henry Parsey as a student and in his early days in medical practice to decide to 'make lunacy his life's work.'[33]

ENDNOTES

1. 'Speaker' Conolly also built a hunting lodge in the Dublin mountains, later used by the Dublin Hell Fire Club for their private meetings.

2. Stern *Three Warwickshire Psychiatrists.*
3. Cowpox vaccination as a method of preventing smallpox virus (*variola*) infection had been introduced by Dr Edward Jenner, a Gloucestershire GP in 1796. Inoculation with smallpox vaccine (variolation) had been the practice heretofore, but the Vaccination Act 1840 banned the practice and introduced infant vaccination free of charge. In 1833 vaccination became compulsory for all children under 12 months of age, parents being subject to a fine for neglecting to protect their children.
4. See Appendix 6.
5. The building is now administrative offices for the Royal Shakespeare Company.
6. The workhouse has been demolished and the hospital in now a hotel.
7. The Trust has since managed to purchase New Place (Shakespeare's last home); Nash's House (the home of Dr Thomas Nash and his wife Elizabeth, Shakespeare's granddaughter); Ann Hathaway's Cottage, the childhood home of Shakespeare's wife, Ann); Arden House (Shakespeare's mother's childhood home) and Hall's Croft (the home of the physician Dr John Hall and his wife Susanna, Shakespeare's daughter).
8. Conolly *A Study of Hamlet.*
9. Quoted in Parry-Jones *Trade in Lunacy* p236.
10. Sir Gray Skipwith, Bt, Recorder of Stratford-upon-Avon 1823-1835 & MP 1831-1835. He was descended through his mother's side from the American Indian Pocohontas; d Hampton Lucy 1852, survived by at least 15 of his 20 children.
11. Conolly *Indications of Insanity.*
12. Valedictory Lecture *London Medical Gazette* 7 May 1831, 161-7.
13. Quoted in Ashton *Victorian Bloomsbury* p44.
14. Together they edited the *British & Foreign Medical Review* from 1836-39, before Conolly departed for Hanwell. Became Queen's Physician, knighted 1813, d 1861.
15. A private asylum near Cheltenham.

16. MRCS 1810; surgeon and founder member of the Provincial Medical & Surgical Assoc.

17. by Thomas Hughes, first published in 1847.

18. The Institute no longer exists and the library has been dispersed.

19. Conolly quoted in Hunter & Macalpine *Three Hundred Years* p24.

20. Conolly *Treatment of the Insane* p95.

21. Conolly quoted in Hunter & Macalpine *Three Hundred Years* p1030.

22. Nicholas Tromans *Richard Dadd* p96.

23. To say nothing of 'the solitary vice'. See Tuke & Bicknill, *Manual of Psych Med*.

24. b 1835 Giggleswick. qUCH. Became foremost psychiatrist of his generation; founded the Maudsley Hospital.

25. Scotland's administrative system for care of lunatics differed from England's.

26. see *online archive 6*, RCPsych.

27. The distinguished Sir James Simpson (1811-1870); Professor of Midwifery at the University of Edinburgh & discoverer of chloroform anaesthesia for childbirth; inventor of Simpson's obstetric forceps.

28. *BMJ* July 15, 1876.

29. Lowe *The Bastilles of England*. A bitter attack on the abuse of committal procedures.

30. The Registered practitioner with the shop in Clare Market was very likely an apothecary who had achieved Registration (on the General Medical Register) via the Licence of the Society of Apothecaries (LSA).

31. Bucknill *The Mad Folk of Shakespeare*.

32. A safe surgical procedure to remove the enlarged prostate gland – and thus restore the outflow of urine from the bladder – would be developed by a TCD surgeon, Terence Millin FRCS. But not until 1945.

33. Obituary of WHP, *Munk's Roll, Royal College of Physicians*.

CHAPTER 4

HATTON'S FIRST MEDICAL SUPERINTENDENT

Henry Parsey's father, John Leveson Parsey, was a Londoner – born in 1793, he had been christened in St Martin-in-the-Fields Church, Trafalgar Square – who described himself as 'gentleman' and was an official in the Home Office. Henry's mother was Matilda Procter, of Pinner, Middlesex, also born in 1793.

They were married on 29 April 1819 in St Margaret's Church, Edgware, by the Rev James Procter, curate at St Margaret's and also Matilda's elder brother: her younger brother William would also become an Anglican clergyman, and would perform the marriage ceremony for his daughter to Henry.

Henry Parsey was born on 3 April 1821 at Hemus Terrace (now Royal Avenue, just off the King's Road), Chelsea, the third of eight children: John James (b 1818); Elizabeth (b 1819); William Henry (b 1821); Charles Frederick (b 1822 but died in infancy); Matilda (b 1825); Harriet (b 1826); Louisa (b 1829); George Frederick (b 1831) and Mary Ann (b 1835).

John James was baptized by his uncle, the Rev James Procter, at St Luke's Parish Church, Chelsea, in June 1818. Elizabeth and Henry were also baptized there (together) in July 1821, and Charles Frederick in January 1823, but on neither of those last two occasions by their uncle.

Matilda and Harriet were also baptized together in July 1826 – once again by the Rev James Procter – but on this occasion at St John's Parish Church, Hampstead, when the family was living, for reasons unknown, in Kilburn.

Hampstead is some distance from Kilburn, so it is difficult to know why the two baptisms took place there, but Hampstead Parish Church has always been fashionable.[1]

Louisa was baptized in August 1829 at St George's, Hanover Square, the parish church of Mayfair.[2] The family appears to have moved house again, this time to Ebury Street in Belgravia; John Leveson was still being described as 'gent.' on the children's birth certificates, so perhaps short leases rather than fluctuating fortunes (in a civil servant?) were the reason for the repeated change of abode.

But by August 1831 the family had returned once more to Chelsea, for George and Mary Ann were both baptized at St Luke's once again, albeit not by the Rev James Procter. The family's address was now Swan Walk (off Royal Hospital Road and bordering the Chelsea Physic Garden): again a fashionable part of town.

SCHOOLING

Henry was educated at Clarence House School, Chelsea and St Peter's Collegiate School, Eaton Square. St Peter's was an Anglican foundation and accepted 'boys aged from six to nineteen from the Upper Classes' ; the Headmaster was required to be 'a graduate of Oxford, Cambridge or Trinity College, Dublin and a clergyman of the United Church of England and Ireland'.

The quality of teaching at St Peter's appears to have been good, and the masters, seemingly, held in high esteem by the pupils; for example, the Rev. Henry Cookesley,

MA (Trinity College, Cambridge), was presented with 'an elegant coffee service of Plate' by the pupils on the occasion of his retirement from the Headmastership.

During Henry's schooldays almost all the teachers appear to have been Cambridge educated men: the Rev William Stoddart, Assistant Master until 1838 (when he became Second Master at Repton School) was a Cambridge MA, and a Scholar of Christ's College; the Rev Richard Wilson, who had been Headmaster at Wigan Grammar School before being appointed Headmaster at St Peter's in 1837, was also a Cambridge MA and a Scholar of St John's. Interestingly, he appears to have combined his Headship at St Peter's with the position of Chaplain to the Chelsea Workhouse.

St Peter's Collegiate School, like many others of that era had a brief existence: established in 1830, 'in union with King's College, London', it closed in 1873, for reasons unknown, dismissing the headmaster, the Rev Burford Gibsone, (another Cambridge MA and a Scholar of Trinity) who retired to a country living in Wolvey, Warwickshire.[3]

Some Anglican schools in Middlesex with a good academic standard, of which St Peter's was one, could apply for 'union with King's College' of the new University of London, thereby allowing their pupils to enter King's College as second-year students.

This was the educational path that Henry took, for the records of King's College show he entered as an Exhibitioner (confirming the quality of education at St Peter's) in October 1837, aged 16, and his being awarded a First Class Bachelor in Arts (University of London) degree in Natural Sciences in June 1840.

London University had been established in 1826 'for the education of students of every creed without distinction'; it was not until 1828 that Oxford and Cambridge eventually accepted non-Anglicans.

London University had opened with one constituent college, University College, in Gower Street (where John Conolly had taught). Even so, providing a purely secular education must have caused some disquiet in the governing body (which no doubt included a number of Anglican clergymen), for a second college, King's, was founded shortly thereafter, in 1829, with a strong Anglican connection.

After being awarded his BA, Henry entered the Medical Department at King's, which in 1840 had opened a teaching hospital, King's College Hospital, in a converted workhouse in Portugal St.[4]

A number of male members of the Parsey family in the past had entered Holy Orders, but Henry was the first in his family to entertain Medicine as a career, as would his son Edward; later generations would invariably choose the Law. Henry continued to have, by any standard, a brilliant student career. In the London University First Examination for MB (Bachelor of Medicine) in August 1842 he was placed in the First Division, with Honours in Anatomy, Physiology and Chemistry. The following year he obtained the First Prize in Medicine, Surgery and Midwifery and was awarded the Warneford Medal for 1843.

THE WARNEFORD MEDALS

The Warneford Medals have an interesting history: in 1838 the Rev Samuel Warneford, (1763-1855), Rector of Bourton-on-the-Hill, in Gloucestershire, an Oxford graduate and 'eccentric but highly practical philanthropist', was a very generous benefactor to a number of medical institutions. His benefactions included an endowment made to the Oxford Lunatic Asylum, built in 1826, (renamed the Warneford Hospital in his honour in 1843), and also an endowment for the building of the 'Warneford General Bathing Institution and Leamington Hospital'.

In the original name of the hospital, 'Bathing Institution' preceded 'Hospital', because the hydrotherapy popularly available at Leamington at the time – a legacy from its heyday as a spa, and the reason behind the town's expansion – took precedence over any other form of treatment.

The site for the hospital in Leamington was donated by Lord Aylesford of Packington Hall and the foundation stone laid in 1832 by Charles Bertie Percy, MP 1826-1829 (of whom, it was said, that he had never taken part in a single debate in the Chamber), and Sheriff of Warwickshire 1835-6.

The new hospital replaced the dispensary in Regent Street which had been built in 1825, and which had become inadequate due to the increased population of the town. Every subscriber of one guinea[5] per annum could recommend two out-patients, 'gratuitous vaccination' was given every week 'to children of the poorer classes', and there was a resident chaplain.

The resident 'house surgeon' was subject to the hospital's rules, as drawn up by the Hospital Board, which stipulated (among other requirements) that the doctor appointed was to be 'free from the care of a family', not to entertain guests on hospital premises without prior permission of the Hospital Board, and to leave word where he might be found whenever he was absent from the building. (It was very much the same for the resident doctors at the asylum).

Notwithstanding such philanthropy to medicine, the Rev Warneford apparently considered medical students to be 'a most godless body of men'[6] and wished to encourage them to try and find evidence for religion in the natural world.

To this end, he donated £1000[7] to King's College London, to establish a prize of a bronze medal to be awarded annually for the best essay by a King's medical student 'on the evidences of natural religion from the facts and laws of the physical universe, especially those parts of it which are connected with medical or anatomical studies; and on the connection and harmony of natural and revealed religion'.

It is still awarded by King's College, but is now a scholarship of £500 a year for five years, no longer accompanied by a bronze medal regrettably, awarded to 'any student who has excelled academically, whilst studying for the "Associate of King's College" diploma, which is a specific King's qualification, involving the study of Theology'.

He also established a similar annual prize for medical students at the new Birmingham Medical School in 1838, once again for essays which were intended to demonstrate 'the pathway of God's wisdom, power and goodness as revealed by their anatomical and other studies'. Some of the essays submitted by Birmingham medical students still survive; they have mind-numbing titles such as:

'The Structure of the Lungs, Anatomically and Physiologically considered, with a view to exemplify or set forth, by Instance or Example, the Wisdom, Power, and Goodness of God, as revealed and declared by Holy Writ.'[8] and discuss anatomy with references to the Scriptures. They do not read very well today.

★

When Henry Parsey received his Warneford Medal at the distribution of Medical Prizes at King's College in 1843, performed by His Grace The Archbishop of Canterbury, Visitor to the College, he was introduced by Dr Todd, Dean of the Medical School in the following terms:

Not the least agreeable part of my duty on the present occasion still remains. This is to present to Your Grace Mr Henry Parsey, who has been unanimously elected by my colleagues the Medical Scholar of this year. The examination which Mr Henry Parsey has passed is of no ordinary kind; and no-one but a man of great attainments and long-continued industry could have acquitted himself at it in so distinguished a manner as Mr Henry Parsey has done. It embraces the whole range of medical sciences, and occupied three days for nearly eight hours each day. Nor is it confined to medical subjects; for the object of the establishment of the Scholarship was to add to those encouragements for the combined cultivation of religious and medical knowledge, which has been founded by the munificence of Dr Warneford; and therefore the candidates are required to pass an examination in Divinity, before they are admitted to the competition in the medical subjects.

(Dr Warneford had further stipulated that 'no award for excellence in other subjects was to compensate for failure in Divinity' – a 'highly practical philanthropist' indeed, and plainly a cautious, if generous, benefactor).

Regrettably, neither Henry Parsey's winning essay nor any other of the King's College Warneford Medal essays have survived.[9]

GRADUATION

The following year, in November 1844, Henry went on to graduate Bachelor of Medicine, with First Class Honours.

Apart from a Post Office Directory of 1848 listing an entry as "Parsey, Wm. Henry, surgeon, 1 Swan Walk, Chelsea" – and it is this entry which suggests he was known as 'Henry',[10] – which indicates he was still living in the family home, nothing further is known of his activities after graduation until the BMJ reported, in February 1846, that he had been become a Licentiate of the Society of Apothecaries. This is the only evidence of any professional activity undertaken by him between November 1844, when he graduated, and 1848, when he took up the post of Assistant Physician to Dr John Bucknill, at the Devon County Asylum in Exminster. It is more than likely he may have worked in King's College Hospital as a junior hospital doctor, but the hospital records do not give the names of junior medical staff, only the Attending Physicians and Surgeons.

Why would he need to become a Licentiate of the Society of Apothecaries: surely a London University degree in medicine was sufficient to practice medicine? Up to a point.

In 1858, the medical profession became regulated by Act of Parliament with the introduction of the General Medical Register. Prior to its introduction 'the grossest anomalies prevailed throughout the United Kingdom'.[11]

In the early 1800s, medical men could practice with very little formal training at all: an apprenticeship to an apothecary could suffice, and in the provinces professional standards were 'variable and generally low'.[12]

Before 1858, only Licentiates or Fellows of the Royal College of Physicians of London could practice as physicians in London. Fellowship of the Royal College of Physicians was awarded only to graduates of Oxford, Cambridge and Trinity College, Dublin but Edinburgh graduates could become Licentiates. Graduates of other Universities were excluded entirely.

Furthermore, the Licence of the Royal College of Physicians of London was considered the only qualification which entitled the holder to practice all the branches of the profession – medicine, surgery and midwifery – and to dispense medicines for patients under his own care. All other persons ineligible to be examined for the Licence and wishing to dispense medicines were obliged to be apprenticed to an apothecary and then be examined for the Licence of the Society of Apothecaries (LSA).

University graduates were able to practice medicine and prescribe (but not dispense) medicines, and thus virtually excluded from acting as general practitioners, who also dispensed medicines, unless they also held the LSA Diploma.

General practitioners were for the main part not University men: they usually served an apprenticeship with an apothecary, and took the LSA Diploma, and frequently the Diploma of the Royal College of Surgeons too.

This dual qualification of MRCS, LSA was often colloquially referred to as 'College and Hall', and allowed holders to term themselves 'surgeon-apothecary'.[13] Presumably Henry took this course of action (as Bucknill had done before him) so that should he ever wish to enter general medical practice, then he would be able to dispense medicines: an essential requirement.

THE DEVON COUNTY LUNATIC ASYLUM

Henry Parsey, whilst a medical student, had plainly been impressed by Conolly's course of lectures at Hanwell (which the *Lancet* later published) and, although he was never to work after qualification at Hanwell under Conolly, he must have made the decision that lunacy would be his life's work either before or soon after qualification, for, despite all his prizes as an undergraduate, he deliberately chose to work as Bucknill's assistant in Exminster, in a branch of medicine which had little social status or indeed much professional respect among the medical world in general at that time. Little has changed.

No doubt he applied himself diligently to his duties in the asylum – and his studies – at Exminster, for he was awarded an MD by London University in 1848.[14] Regrettably, no records survive in the National Archives regarding his years in Devon under Bucknill.

MARRIAGE

His success in being appointed to the position of Medical Superintendent at Hatton must have given him enough security to consider embarking on family life, for on 20 January 1852, he requested leave of the Visitors 'to be absent from 26th inst. until the end of February'. This they granted, and on 5 February 1852, aged 31 (or of 'full age' as the marriage certificate states), he was married in All Saints Church, Bishop Burton, near Beverley, in the County of York, to Julia Procter, aged 30, by the Rev William Procter, Julia's father. They were first cousins, Julia's father being the younger brother of Henry's mother, Matilda, and his maternal uncle.

William Procter had been Vicar of All Saints, Bishop Burton for some years, and Julia had been living in the Vicarage with her parents and younger sister, Louisa and brother, Lovell – who was also to become an Anglican minister – who were both witnesses on the marriage certificate.

At the end of February, the couple returned to Warwickshire to continue making preparations for the reception of patients into the Asylum.

THE HATTON ASYLUM OPENS

'A man and his wife to the name of Steele, late of the Surrey County Lunatic Asylum', were appointed Principal

Attendants – 'the man at £30 and his wife at £14 per annum' – on the recommendation of Sir Alexander Morrison, Attending Physician to the Surrey asylum. Henry Parsey had then to turn his attention towards more mundane matters: providing surgical instruments, invalid bedding and telltale clocks (which recorded the times of attendants visits to the wards during the night), and also having padded rooms prepared for difficult patients.

On a more positive pastoral note, a non-resident Chaplain, the Rev Charles Wood was duly appointed (as we have seen). His duties were 'to perform Divine Service and preach one sermon on every Sunday, also to read prayers on at least two days in the week and to attend patients whom the Medical Superintendent shall consider to be in a proper state of mind'.

The opening of the Asylum for the reception of patients appears to have been a somewhat hurried affair, for June saw Dr Parsey and Mr Crofts (the Clerk of Works) striving towards 'the completion of two wards with airing courts, together with kitchens, laundry and offices necessary for the admission of a limited number of patients on 29 June'.

But open it did on 29 June 1852, albeit still in a somewhat unfinished state, with staff in post which comprised Dr Parsey, a matron & housekeeper (and her servant), a clerk & steward, an engineer, a bailiff & gardener (whose wife acted as dairymaid), a brewer & baker (who also acted as lodgekeeper), a house porter, a cook, two laundrymaids, two male attendants, two female attendants and a chaplain. All the above, except for the chaplain, were provided with accommodation, washing, coal, fire and light; and for the Medical Superintendent, 'vegetables and hay for one horse'.

By the end of the first week, three males and three females had been admitted from Northampton Lunatic

Hospital, where they were being cared for at the County's expense, and just over a month later, by 5 August, there were twenty male patients and thirty three female.

During this initial period of clinical activity, more administrative tasks required Dr Parsey's supervision; Henry Pepys, Lord Bishop of Worcester was approached for a licence for the Chapel, 'for the performance and celebration of Divine Service in the said building, according to the Rubrick of the Church of England and not otherwise or in any other manner' which was granted on 9 August, and the chaplain was requested to provide a surplice, two dozen prayer books stamped 'Warwick County Lunatic Asylum' on the front cover and a linen Communion cloth for the altar table, together with a silver Communion Service (which was purchased from a Mr Enoch, Silversmith, of Warwick).

A burial ground, for the burial of those patients dying in the Asylum and who had not been removed by their relatives for burial elsewhere, was marked out and fenced, to await consecration by the Bishop of Worcester – which he eventually performed, but not until January 1855, after considerable correspondence had passed between the asylum and the Bishop's Office.

Finally, Dr Parsey ordered 'a bagatelle table, four sets of common draughtsmen, four boxes of dominos and four boxes of "fox and geese" (an ancient board game of strategy played by two unequally opposed players – one fox *versus* fifteen geese) for the amusement of the patients', and the following periodicals – 'Illustrated London News' (still a hardy perennial of dentists' waiting rooms today), 'Punch', a humorous and satirical magazine which was 'a staple of British drawing rooms', (probably because of its inoffensive nature), 'The Home' magazine and, with advice from the Chaplain, 'an initial selection of books from the Religious

Tract Society, to form the foundation of a library from which inmates [sic] may draw for amusement and instruction'.

★

The Commissioners in Lunacy made their first visit to the Asylum on 14 December 1852, after six months of activity: there were one hundred and twenty six patients in residence; of these, thirty three males were employed in 'spade labour and other work' and forty eight females in household work. After commenting on various matters, they concluded:

> The patients are generally tranquil, and no coercion is used and their condition is generally healthy.[15]

The following year the Commissioners in Lunacy reported:

> Altogether the Asylum is in a good and promising state and does credit to the diligence and skill of the Superintendent.[16]

By this time, December 1853, there were one hundred and eighty seven patients resident, of whom 62 males and 74 females had been removed from other asylums, 10 males and 10 females from Union houses, 44 males and 42 females from their homes; one male had been admitted from the County Gaol, two had been admitted immediately on their discharge from gaol, and one patient admitted as 'a wandering lunatic'.

The medical diagnoses were as follows (the quotations are from Dr Parsey's first report to the Visitors of 1853):

> 52 patients were admitted with 'acute mania' ('a disease which though sometimes rapidly fatal presents, under careful treatment and

if uncomplicated by epilepsy or serious organic disease, a far greater prospect of recovery than any other form of mental disorder').

149 were admitted in a state of 'chronic mania' or 'dementia' ('who constitute the bulk of the inmates of all asylums ... and their labour can be turned to valuable account in either indoor or outdoor industrial occupations and from their protracted residence and practical knowledge of the routine discipline of an Asylum... and general ready obedience, are extremely useful in the conducing to good order and tranquility').

19 admissions were for 'melancholia' ('either as depression combined with fixed delusion on some specific train of thought or feeling, when it may be more appropriately designated monomania, or as depression unconnected with appreciable delusion but leading to a disgust of life and determination to self-destruction, which more directly belongs to the state termed moral insanity in which without any marked derangement of the intellectual faculties the moral feelings impulses and affections are so perverted as to render isolation from society necessary').

19 patients were congenital idiots ('few but the lowest type of idiot find their way into asylums before they have passed the period of youth...it is very doubtful whether any real benefit would accrue to them unless they were placed in a distinct department with attendants and teachers whose whole time could be devoted to their care and instruction'). [In later years this this would become a matter for further consideration by Dr Parsey and the Visitors].

34 of the cases were complicated with epilepsy and 7 with general paralysis: 'the former of these complications almost precludes the hope of recovery and numbers amongst its victims the most troublesome, vicious and dangerous inmates of the asylum; the latter though brought under treatment in its early stages pursues its course to a fatal termination little affected by the different means adopted to arrest its progress'.

But it was not all doom and gloom: by the end of 1853, the first full year, thirty six patients had been discharged 'recovered', and a further four discharged 'much improved'.

Dr John Conolly, by now the 'late Visiting Physician of the Hanwell Lunatic Asylum', on a visit to the asylum, expressed to Dr Parsey his 'approbation of the building and his great gratification at the system of medical treatment adopted throughout the establishment'.[17]

Plainly, Conolly had taught his former pupil well.

★

All very satisfactory and an encouraging start to Henry Parsey's administration, one would think, but all was not as it appeared.

There may well have been some form of personality clash or other cause of major dispute between him and the Matron, Eliza Turkington. This is only surmise, but, for reasons unknown, in December 1852 he was granted permission by the Visitors to be allowed to become a candidate for the office of Medical Superintendent of the new Essex County Lunatic Asylum, which was to open at Brentwood in 1853, providing accommodation for three hundred patients. He was unsuccessful in his bid to move to Essex, and perhaps attempts were made to heal the breach between them (if there had been one), but Matron, and her servant, Margaret Hurst, were to resign their posts, together (again for reasons unknown) on 1 February 1854.

The early years of the Asylum were to be quite unsettled as far as staffing and clinical care of the patients were concerned: upon Eliza Turkington's resignation in February 1854, Harriet Bakewell was appointed Matron on the following day – an extraordinarily swift appointment – but she too was to resign precipitately on 2 August, within three months of her appointment, again for reasons unknown.

The third Matron, Frances Close, survived in post for not very long either; similarly appointed Matron on the day following Harriet Bakewell's resignation, she too resigned on 4 Feb 1857, after 3 years in post. The asylum's Register of Employees states baldly 'Committed for dishonesty. Bailed and indicted but did not appear.'

Perhaps it was all too much for Henry Parsey to cope with, for the BMJ briefly reported on 14 December 1855, that Dr Bowers, the Assistant Medical Officer at the Stafford County Lunatic Asylum (which had opened in 1818), had been elected the new Medical Superintendent on the retirement of Dr James Wilkes (who incidentally, had won a Warneford Medal in 1832, whilst a student at Birmingham School of Medicine, for an essay on 'The Great Sympathetic Nerve'), and that there had been thirty two applicants for the office, which had been reduced to a short list of three – 'Dr H Parsey, Warwick; J Buck Esq, Leicester; and Dr Bowers', (the local candidate winning the post).

Presumably, this was yet another unsuccessful attempt to leave the Hatton asylum.

During this period of internal upheavals, his academic career nevertheless progressed steadily following his MD whilst at Exminster, with the award of Membership of the Royal College of Physicians in 1855 (and Fellowship in 1877).

Fortunately the fourth Matron, Louisa Raynes, who had been appointed in 1857, was to bring some stability to the care of the female patients, for she stayed at the asylum for twenty years, until her retirement in 1877.

There had always been a tension between the Union houses and asylums: Union houses (workhouses) were administered via the Poor Law, and their Superintendents and attached Medical Officers determined who should (and who should not) be referred to the asylum, despite a legal requirement to refer within fourteen days of admission all lunatics admitted to a Union house: for the harmless – ie idiots and imbeciles – and more manageable lunatics it was more expedient and less expensive not to do so.

Likewise the Union houses were beholden to receive those lunatics discharged from the asylum, whether 'recovered', 'improved' or 'uncured', if they could not return to their own homes or to the care of relatives or friends.

Asylums, on the other hand, were administered by Justices of the Peace via the Quarter Sessions and the Committee of Visitors, an overview being provided by the Commissioners in Lunacy in London.

Dr Parsey's first Annual Report, delivered on 25 December 1853, details how during the first year of the asylum's operation, all lunatics chargeable to the different Unions in the County and previously confined in other asylums or 'mad-houses' were removed to Hatton, the remaining admissions coming from either the Union houses or directly from their homes.

Admission to the asylum of a patient under the 1845 Lunacy Act would be requested of the Medical Superintendent by an Order of Admission signed by a Justice of the Peace (or an 'Officiating Clergyman of the Parish' and the Relieving Officer of the Parish or Union in which the person was residing), together with a doctor's certificate of insanity.[18]

A study of the male and female Orders of Admission for 1852, shows that all persons admitted to the asylum were admitted with Orders made by Justices and the relevant Relieving Officer on every occasion (apart from one patient admitted on the order of the Home Secretary); on no occasion was a member of the Clergy required to certificate.

All but one of the lunatics who had been confined in other asylums were admitted from those in the neighbouring Counties, the exception being one lunatic admitted from

Grove Hall Asylum, in Bow, a private madhouse, whence he had been admitted from Bethlem Hospital, where all patients were discharged after a period of twelve months, whether cured or not: he had been admitted with 'melancholia', so presumably was 'uncured'. A number of others came from private mad-houses in Hunningham, Hook Norton, and a cohort of sixteen patients 'chargeable to the United Parishes of St Michael and the Holy Trinity, Coventry, now being confined in the House licensed for the reception of lunatics known as White House Lunatic Asylum situate in Bethnal Green'.[19] None came from any of the madhouses in Henley-in-Arden, however; the clientele in those houses were not paupers and thus ineligible for admission.

Of the 140 Orders of Admissions studied, there were 99 lunatics (one 'lunatic' was a male, aged 45, who had come from the Hook Norton madhouse, where he had been 'lunatic since birth': plainly the diagnostic terms were loosely applied and very much interchangeable), 27 persons of unsound mind (which sometimes included idiots), 13 idiots or imbeciles, one insane epileptic, and 11 minors aged under 21 (the youngest was an idiot boy aged 5), and a certain William Winkles.

He, after indictment for larceny, had been considered to be insane on arraignment and been temporarily removed from gaol to the asylum at Hunningham (which had seventy beds and was, prior to the opening of the asylum, probably the most secure institution in the County as the residents were accommodated in purpose-built outbuildings).

Dr Parsey had received the following directive from the Home Secretary, Spencer Horatio Walpole, on 4 November 1852, for William Winkles' admission to the Asylum:

Application is now being made for admission to the WCLA (and let it be distinctly understood that the expense of this person's maintenance therein will not be defrayed by the Government). He is to remain in custody until further order shall be made herein.

Although Bethlem Hospital housed the majority of the criminally insane, it was not unusual for Hatton and other county asylums to admit some too, until Broadmoor Asylum for the Criminally Insane opened in 1863. Bethlem Hospital then became an asylum for the 'superior class', and atoned for its past errors by gaining an excellent reputation for the quality of its care. (Dr Parsey was to speak highly of it in the following year).[20]

★

One female minor, aged 17, was admitted suffering from 'moral insanity with a strong hysterical diathesis' who had been for years an inmate of the Union house, 'whence she had been sentenced six times to the House of Correction for periods ranging from three weeks to two months'; she had also been subjected to the most rigid discipline of the workhouse in order to correct what was considered to be 'her perverse and sullen temper and wild vagaries'.

Dr Parsey was able to report that she greatly improved under the regime of the Asylum, and became useful, industrious and generally well-conducted, though she was still subject to 'occasional perversion of feeling, which she however successfully strives to overcome'.[21]

Dr Parsey paints an optimistic picture of her, soon after her admission to the asylum, in his Report for the Visitors, but then we hear no more of her; was she eventually discharged 'recovered' or 'improved', as might be the inference? Her records survive, and they merit closer perusal: firstly, how exactly was her admission to the asylum effected?

She was a servant by the name of Hannah Smith, aged seventeen, from Allesley, a village near Coventry. She was admitted to the Asylum as a 'lunatic' under an Order of Admission signed by a Justice of the Peace and the Relieving Officer together with a medical certificate[22] signed by the Poor Law Medical Officer for Allesley Parish, Dr Jonathan Kimbell, a general practitioner of Knowle.[23]

The Order indicates that her current illness was of six weeks duration but not of a suicidal nature nor did she pose a threat to the safety of others, and this was her first admission to an asylum. The medical certificate stated Hannah was a 'lunatic', and 'a proper person to be confined', (one of five legal categories defined as 'lunatic', 'person of unsound mind', 'insane person', 'idiot' or 'imbecile') and although personal examination of the patient by the attending physician on the day of certification was a legal requirement, no medical reasons for the doctor's diagnosis of 'proper person to be confined' were required on the certificate.

That was soon to change: within a year, an amendment to the 1845 Lunacy Act made it a requirement that every doctor signing an Order of Admission must document 'facts indicating insanity as observed by myself' and 'other facts indicating insanity communicated by to me by others'. After a 'proper person' had been admitted to the asylum, a copy of the Order of Admission had to be sent to the Commissioners in Lunacy in London to be scrutinized and they had the powers to dispute any medical certificate which appeared to them to be unsatisfactory.

So far, so good, as far as the legal paperwork for committal was concerned. But what of the patient? The case notes record her admission and initial assessment by the Assistant Medical Officer and chronicle thereafter – not particularly assiduously – her behaviour and management whilst in the asylum:

"July 8 1852 Hannah Smith, aged 17, single, inmate of workhouse, member of established church. Has been many times in House of Correction at Warwick.[24] Heavy expression and is evidently weakminded. In good general health and condition, short, full face, clear fair complexion; appetite good.

August 2 In a day or two she lost the moroseness of manner she had when admitted and subsided into a quiet cheerful manner and willingness to make herself useful. She continued to improve until 27th when she again became wilful, morose and somewhat moody. On the following three days she passed through a paroxysm of hysterical mania on the first day continually screaming and crying, destroying clothing, attempted to bang her head against the wall, had fanciful delusions about imaginary objects and the conduct of other patients to her. She then returned to her tranquil state but with some moroseness and wilfulness.

[Hannah was here prescribed medication but the prescriptions in the record book are indecipherable].

August 11 Has returned to her previous tranquil condition but if at all put out or interfered with becomes irritable wilful and abusive: by tact and good management she is generally kept quiet usefully employed by the nurse.

During her admission her diagnosis was refined from the catch-all term 'lunatic' to 'moral insanity with a strong hysterical diathesis'.

'Strong hysterical diathesis' indeed. She must have been quite a handful to manage: the asylum recorded every episode of restraint or seclusion of a patient in a 'Journal of Restraint/Seclusion and Medical Treatment'. This register, signed weekly by Dr Parsey, was a statutory requirement; although it is available only from the opening of the asylum until the end of December 1857 – and no patient appears ever to have required restraint – Hannah Smith featured regularly in the list of those few patients requiring seclusion.

Hannah first featured on 27 August 1852, some six weeks after her admission, when she was kept in seclusion for three hours. This was repeated the following day, and again in September and December, on each occasion for three hours.

Most annual reports of the Commissioners in Lunacy detail the numbers of patients secluded (and the duration) since their last inspection, and indeed, when resorted to, seclusion appears to have been used merely for hours rather than days:

> Seclusion has been employed on four occasions since the last visit, and for a total of 14 hours [which amounts to 3½ hours per episode] among the male patients and on 61 occasions for 354 hours [just under 6 hours per episode], and one female has been mechanically restrained during 12 nights, and another during 2 nights and a day. in both cases for surgical reasons.[25]

What did seclusion entail? Conolly's practice at Hanwell was to place the patient alone in a quiet ordinary sleeping room, with regular visual inspections from attendants through an observation hatch in the door; in extreme cases the patient would be placed in a room of which the floor was a bed, and the four walls padded: the room was not always darkened, and was never completely dark.[26] No doubt Dr Parsey's practice would have been very similar.

In 1853 she spent some 120 hours over nineteen days in seclusion; although the intervals between episodes of seclusion increased, the duration of seclusion increased too.

Reasons for seclusion were added to entries from 1854 onwards, and Hannah's reasons included 'maniacal excitement and extreme indecency'; 'maniacal excitement and destructiveness' or 'hysterical excitement'.

Interestingly, other reasons for seclusion included 'violence to nurse'; 'obscene language and conduct'; and 'violence to fellow patient'.

The shower bath was used very infrequently, being recorded as a punishment for 'wilfully breaking glass' or 'attempting to escape'.

And it should be explained that personal restraint was still used in the context of preventing a patient from tearing at and removing surgical dressings or bandages, but this was considered to be perfectly acceptable: indeed it is still considered so in practice today.

October 4 Has had since last report two attacks similar to August 2nd but neither of them of too intense a character. The first was about the latter end of August and the second at the latter end of September and attended the catamenal period [as the menstrual cycle was then termed], the first that has occurred since the middle of July. It came with a great pain in the back and lower part of the abdomen, was abundant and passed off in five days.

She was at first crying, moaning and much depressed with the pain. Since then catamen has ceased she has been having shower baths every morning with advantage. She has now returned to her normal latency.

2 February 1853 Since last report pt. has had no period of continuous excitement. She has varied a good deal, often being irritable and requiring much management and has occasionally had from a few hours to a day or two much active excitement of an hysterical character; at those times has been abusive and destructive of clothing and extremely noisy and restless at night.

28 February Was ordered a warm bath every night with a shower of cold water to the head. She expresses herself relieved by this treatment.

1 April Another attack, intellect clear but moral feelings extremely perverted; language abusive and filthily obscene, all her actions extremely impulsive. Her animal diet has recently been lowered.

[Presumably the thinking behind this was that less red meat in the diet would render the patient less likely to be aggressive]

3 June During the latter part of April and May she was comparatively tranquil and very useful but very impulsive.

3 October Tranquil, orderly and making great efforts at self-control, in the hope she may be able to leave here [Regrettably, this event did not come to pass] but still occasional hysterical attacks.

[More prescriptions, again indecipherable].

7 December Generally easily managed with tact. During her attacks is suicidal – attempted to suspend herself from window and strangle herself.

[Entries in the case book now become very infrequent].

14 April 1854 Precisely the same as on previous occasions.
September 1 Since last report she has been extremely variable; has made greater efforts at self-control especially during past 4-5 months. She has been generally employed in the kitchen but very capriciously. At times delusional that people are tapping at the floor or ceiling during the night.

[The next entry in the case book was made, somewhat apologetically, after an interval of six years and ten months].

July 1862 No entry has been made as mental state has been precisely the same as on former occasions. At times she has very strong delusions.

[Following this report, the interval until the next entry is only five years].

1867 No recent change has taken place in the general character of this case. During her excitements is suicidal and tries to suspend herself from the window and strangle herself.

1868 During latter part of summer was in a most precarious state of health. Sickness, purging and great prostration which for a time seemed likely to prove fatal. She however slowly recovered and resumed much her ordinary state.

June 1870 In better health and has for some time conducted herself much better.

December 1872 Continues much in her old state: very hypochondriacal and complaining and very troublesome at times, much put out if not sympathized with. For the last year has had subcutaneous injection of morphine ½ grain [30mg: which is quite a substantial dose: today an average sized adult of 70kg would receive one third or half that dose] to produce sleep at night, but is on the whole in fair health, although has frequent attacks of diarrhoea.

May 1874 Paroxysms of temper not so frequent and when they do occur she can barely control herself. Is very subject to dyspepsia. She is however a very useful ward helper. Loses her temper if she does not get her injection regularly every evening.

January 26 1876 Generally easily managed if not thwarted.

June 2 1877 No change except decidedly quieter of late. Is however very capricious and when offended uses strong language: this is however done deliberately. Is a great reader and employs herself chiefly 'novel reading'.

June 14 1878 For some time has been quite failing in health. [there have been a few comments in the notes regarding her having piles which bleed and also heavy menstrual periods]. She is very anaemic. Her condition is aggravated by utter inattention to all medical directions. She is very wilful and will take no medicines unless she likes it. Is fond of telling the AMO of her rectal state and her catamen loss. Fainted in Day Room today and appeared on arrival of MO to be moribund. She revived however under stimulants. When she became conscious and found brandy was being given to her to revive her she became worse again [underlined – the person making the clinical entry in her notes was clearly exasperated by her].

May 6 1879 Has just passed through a severe attack of pleuropneumonia. She is now as usual. It is difficult to do anything for her as she is very wilful.
November 17 Little change, but has become blanched through loss of blood [from piles and heavy menstrual bleeding]. Is obstinate, wilful and capricious. She will do nothing she is told to nor will she take what medicines etc may be ordered.
Yesterday evening she was very weak and cold at evening visit. Later on she became cold, pulseless, screaming repeatedly and gasping as if for breath. She did not rally and died about 1am this morning.
Cause of Death: Polymenorrhagia of uterus[27]
(signed) Arthur Law Wade MB Assistant Medical Officer" [28]

Despite Hannah's own attempts (and those of the asylum's physicians) at controlling her 'wild vagaries' during the early years of her admission it suggests from the notes she gave up hope of being discharged and resigned herself to indefinite asylum care: a place of safety, certainly, and preferable to the workhouse, with its inflexible rules and punishments for disorderly behaviour and the like (using obscene language, threatening or insulting behaviour, wilful disobedience etc. – to all of which she was prone whilst in the asylum), and which would have resulted in her being required to wear 'penal dress', or some other distinguishing mark of disgrace, for 48 hours and the substitution of '8oz. bread or 1lb. cooked potatoes and the withholding of butter, cheese, tea, sugar or broth for any meal which the miscreant would otherwise receive over a 24 hour period'. 'Refractory behaviour' – the same, or a similar, offence repeated within seven days – would result in solitary confinement for 24 hours in addition.[29]

Little 'tact and good management' to be found in the workhouse, without a doubt. And certainly none at all in the House of Correction.

Episodic seclusion in the asylum seems to have been the least of many evils. Her resignation to – and frustration with – asylum life probably contributed to her continued episodes of uncontrollable hysterical and self-injuring behaviour.

Realization that, despite her best efforts – as we are led to believe from her case notes – she was destined to spend her adult life inside the asylum until her death, which came, after twenty seven years of confinement, at the age of 44 (then the average age for female life expectancy) would probably have led to her continued outbursts of ungovernable temper. Poor Hannah – 'when she was good she was very, very good, but when she was bad she was horrid'.[30] But, without doubt, life would have been a lot worse outside the asylum.

Surprisingly, she appears to have been quite literate, apparently reading novels, so she presumably had more than a modicum of intelligence, despite being described on admission as 'weak-minded' (but that may just have been the admitting Medical Officer's first impression: most likely she was just being sullen and unco-operative). One might have expected that, in the fullness of time, she could been discharged from the asylum, as she had hoped, but her paroxysms of temper were probably very impressive –

and risky – so would hardly be conducive to her returning to a position of household servant; and one fears a career of prostitution would have been the only alternative and an early death was, apparently, the inevitable outcome for those women 'who have taken the primrose path that leads to the everlasting bonfire', as it was so delicately described by a contemporary moralist. To say nothing of suicide from plain desperation.

Hannah developed a deathly pallor in her last days – 'blanched through loss of blood' – and her final symptoms and signs suggest she died from circulatory collapse due to an extreme degree of anaemia incompatible with life. One can only surmise at the degree of psychological damage the workhouse and the House of Correction must have inflicted on her, to make her so impossible to deal with, even unto the last.

As we have seen, age was no barrier to admission: the 1845 Lunacy Act gave no minimum age for admission to an asylum. It was common for idiots and imbeciles to be taken as children into the asylum, when they could not be managed at home ('without being shut up in a cupboard' as one over-taxed mother had stated). Likewise, epileptics were usually admitted in childhood or in their teens, once again, for very sensible reasons, given their likely home circumstances, the fact that there was no effective treatment available to reduce the frequency of seizures, and with current medical opinion that repeated seizures caused an epileptic to regress relentlessly into idiocy.

Under the terms of the 1845 Lunacy Act, a correctly completed Order for Admission to an asylum could not be refused, and indeed Dr Parsey's practice was to admit any patient referred to him if at all possible, 'unless either a patient is presented under the order of a person not having legal authority to commit to the asylum, or when the medical certificate is rendered null and void by the certifying medical man not being able to state any indication of insanity observed by himself at the time of examination'.

Only under these two circumstances was he obliged to refuse admission – as in the case reported in the Leamington Spa Courier in June 1881: a young man had been brought before the Stratford-upon-Avon Borough Court on a charge of 'stealing three cigars, one pork pie and two cakes from the railway station'. He 'conducted himself violently and made use of bad language in court' and a medical man was sent for who pronounced him to be of unsound mind and not responsible for his actions. The charge of felony could not thus be sustained and there was no alternative but to send him to the asylum.

Dr Parsey refused to admit him because the Order for Admission was signed by a borough magistrate, who only had powers to commit a person to a borough asylum, not a County Asylum. As Stratford did not have a borough asylum, he informed them the county Justices should make the order, 'quoting an Act of Parliament'. (This caused quite a commotion when Dr Parsey's refusal to admit was reported to the Court the following week: eventually it was decided to refer the matter to the Secretary of State. Presumably the young man remained in custody in the interim. The Secretary of State's decision is unknown, but he may have made a personal order for admission, as had been the case with William Wilkes, or perhaps he just applied common sense and suggested that a county Justice make the Order for Admission).[31]

Dr Parsey's handwritten response – on County Lunatic Asylum headed notepaper – to a letter of criticism of his decision to refuse admission in such circumstances from a certain Mr J Lane is exemplary in its moderate tone:

'Dear sir,

I beg to acknowledge the receipt of your letter of 4th July with enclosure; and so long as the law remains as at present, will act on the opinion so expressed by the Commissioners in Lunacy, endorsed by the Home Secretary, as to the functions of Magistrates of Boroughs without a Recorder and Quarter Sessions in the matter of ordinary pauper lunatics, lunatics not under proper control, and lunatics wandering at large.

I shall be obliged by your giving your bench my assurance that during the thirty years that I have had the Superintendance of this Asylum it has been my desire to do everything within the limits of the law to facilitate the admission of patients.

The only two contingencies in which I am compelled to temporarily refuse admission are (1) when a patient is presented under the order of a person not having legal authority to commit to the asylum; and (2) when the Medical Certificate is rendered null and void by the certifying medical man not being able to state any indication of insanity observed by himself at the time of examination.

Though there is little possibility of a pauper patient being in a position to bring an action for false imprisonment against the persons concerned in sending to and receiving into an asylum, I dare say you are aware that actions have been sustained and penalties enforced for irregularities or omissions in the order of commitment of apparently a most trifling character.

I am again, Sir,
Yours faithfully,
[signed] W H Parsey

★

One of Henry Parsey's earlier Reports to the Visitors (that of April 1856) confirms how conscientious he was in his management of the Asylum and encapsulates the contemporary philosophy of alienists and is quoted almost in its entirety:

Aided by the great advantage of locality…I have endeavored to pursue the system of treatment, which experience of late years has indicated as most conducive to the recovery of the unfortunate class, for whose wants this institution has been erected, and is best calculated to promote preservation of life, and restoration to some amount of intelligence, and social comfort of the large number, whose lot it will be to pass the remainder of their days as its inmates. The broad principle to be kept in view in the treatment of insanity, and to which all our resources, whether moral, hygienic, or in the more restricted sense medical, ought to be applied is – in recent cases, to restore, as quickly as possible, the equilibrium of the nervous system, and at the same time to endeavour so to improve the general health, as to maintain this equilibrium when restored – [and] in chronic cases to place the system in as favourable a condition as possible to promote a high standard of health, to improve disordered functions, and to remove, where practicable the corrupt secretions and deposits.

[Victorian alienists thinking was still very much that mental illness was a physical disease, despite very little anatomical evidence ever being found to support this theory from the numerous autopsies and microscopic analysis of nervous system tissue which Dr Parsey and others performed diligently in their quest for confirmatory evidence.]

Much is contributed to towards the successful treatment of the disease by the complete revolution of feeling in ideas, often consequent upon the sudden introduction of an insane person to Asylum life, by the change of scene and diet and by the diversion of thought, introduced by the various means of employment and, most important, as soon as the mind can be awakened to an appreciation of their meaning.

At this point the treatment merges into that of the chronic or incurable cases; the means applicable to the improvement of the one being equally so to the recovery of the other. All reasonable inducements are held out for them to engage in the various forms of industrial labour and domestic employment, in accordance with their different capacities. For the men, garden or agricultural work is the most desirable occupation whilst some are advantageously engaged in different trades, such as shoemaking, tailoring, carpentering, assisting the engineer, baker, or painter, or in making themselves useful in the wards. The labour of some of the insane may thus be turned to very profitable account, though, in providing employment for them, the quantity of work to be got through ought to be a very minor consideration to the fact of being able to give occupation for the body without more stress for the mind often may help to draw it into new and cheerful trains of thought. The more active of the insane must be busy at something; if not at work, [then] at mischief, and with the more lethargic the great object is to arouse and exercise their torpid faculties; and to this interest in the treatment of insanity, the satisfaction derived from observing a person passing out of active mania, or a confirmed melancholic, for the first time taking a broom to sweep a few yards of floor, is far greater than that of seeing the most robust incurable do a hard day's work.

Among the females, the laundry and the kitchen, needle and domestic work, afford an ample source of employment; and the records of many Asylums show that of the necessary work for the Establishment is mainly by their exertion performed within its walls – a result advantageous in itself, and gratifying, as showing that a large proportion of them must be more or less usefully engaged.

Pleasing and varied scenery, so cheering and tranquillizing in its effects on the mind, is ensured by the locality of the Asylum; and by the walks about the country, to which a large number look forward, more especially on a part of Sunday not appropriate to divine service. This, also, served to break the monotony, which must otherwise, to some degree attach to Sunday in the wards of the Asylum, many of the inmates not being able to regard it an any other light than as their idle day.

[The good Doctor's description of 'Sunday in the wards' could well apply to any English Public School up until the late 1960s, except that the abolition of physical methods of control of the inmates [sic] therein was still a long time coming].

> *Several of the cheaper periodicals are regularly supplied and, in addition to Bibles and Prayer Books, a number of instructive and amusing books are kept in circulation. Weekly meetings for dancing and singing in which the two sexes are assembled together, the rearing and tending of flowers in the windows, which throughout the asylum are free from wire guards or any other defence – out and indoor games, such as cricket, skittles, quoits, bowls, bagatelle, and draughts – are the means chiefly relied on to promote health and good feeling, and to keep in abeyance those mental peculiarities, which, if not provided with some cheerful and amusing facilities that display themselves would be a constant source of anger, quarrels, and turbulence. So far as their condition will allow of which all are made to feel themselves treated as persons responsible for their actions; and this is only in accordance with the mental capacities of a large number of them; for those more immediately connected with their delusions, or on the sudden outbursts of uncontrollable impulses, many are quite capable of appreciating their own motives of action, and the inferences brought to bear on them, shall be in all matters of self-interest.*

[Dr Parsey was the first Medical Superintendent to institute mixed social activities – dances and suchlike – within an asylum, but under constant supervision from the attendants, of course. This brought him almost universal disapproval by his contemporaries, initially, but which proved in the event to be very popular with staff and patients alike].

> *Under this treatment of management I can conscientiously say that tranquility and good order are the general characteristics of the inmates of this asylum; and, with attendants trained to look upon this as the*

means of preserving discipline, sudden paroxysms of excitement and violence that must occasionally occur are good-temperedly allayed. Seclusion in their rooms is rarely required to be resorted too; indeed, very rarely with the men, though with one or two of the women of unusual excitable temperament occasional recourse to it is found serviceable. The withholding of ordinary indulgences is a common way of checking breaches of discipline. Mechanical restraint is unknown in the Asylum: as a means of coercion for the preservation of discipline, it is in my opinion utterly unjustifiable in a properly constructed Asylum, with an efficient staff of attendants, and a means of protection to the patients from attempted or threatened self-inflicted injuries. I believe it can always be safely disposed with; but it may be not only useful, but essential, where insanity is complicated with some bodily injury which demands for its recovery patient quietude, which the patient will not voluntarily allow. Such a case has, however, not been made under treatment here. I have not appended any statistical tables of minute detail in connection with the results of treatment, as they more appropriately accompany the Report I am required annually to make to the Committee of Visitors of progress and working of the Asylum.

W. H. PARSEY MD

M.O. and Superintendent

3 April 1856

ANIMALS IN THE ASYLUM

Were there any animals in the Hatton asylum?

We know that animals had a long tradition of being found in workhouses[32] and asylums, not least from the lame excuse regarding the shackling and restraint of James Norris at Bethlem Hospital, which had caused such outrage in 1815. James Hadfield too, confined in Bethlem for thirty nine years following his attempt to shoot King

George III at the Theatre Royal, Haymarket in 1800, spent his time writing verses on the deaths of his cats and birds, which were his only companions in the Hospital. A visitor commented:

> He has had in succession two dogs, three cats, birds, and finally a squirrel. He loved these animals dearly, and suffered grief at seeing them die; he has stuffed them himself, and set them up in his room. [33]

Birds and tame animals had been encouraged in the Hanwell Asylum by Conolly, who realised they promoted 'health and good feeling' among the residents (and staff, too, no doubt) and apparently had a caged bird to sing to him while he worked in his office in the asylum – quite a common practice in the Victorian era – and suggested:

> buildings containing birds of various kinds, and tame animals, would be found to interest many of the patients. A piece of shallow water, with ducks and other aquatic fowl would also give them pleasure. [34]

★

In 1855 a Mary Robinson was admitted to Morningside Asylum in Edinburgh 'after following a course of extravagance and dissipation'. She remained very disruptive, and in 1860 continued to 'take a kind of pleasure in destroying everything she can e.g. she broke a tree in the airing court and on one occasion tried to throw the cat out of the window'. (She became a permanent resident, dying in the asylum in 1888).

In 1860 the Illustrated London News published an engraving of the men's ward at Bethlem Hospital in which 'two slightly wary looking whippets, or small greyhounds, are wandering among the patients, while one of them keeps a watchful eye on a cat seated beside the chair of a chess player. At intervals along the walls are birdcages and goldfish bowls all with their appropriate occupants.' The dogs may have belonged to Dr Charles Hood, the Resident Physician (of whom Dr Parsey spoke highly), but birds and animals by this time, the 1860s, were regarded as a normal part of hospital life.[35]

In 1890 a Florence Wakeley, aged 20, was admitted to Bethlem Hospital with melancholia and auditory hallucinations and remained agitated on the ward, although she recovered and was discharged within six months. On admission

> She took a parrot out of its cage and wrung its neck but was unable to explain why she had done it. It was also recorded that she tried to kiss one of the clinical assistants.

(Always a hazard for young hospital doctors).

The Visitors may not have been overtly enthusiastic, but they did consider that singing birds, pet animals and pictures on the wall 'minor subjects of interest', (for this, much thanks), and thought that 'taken collectively, they were the outward signs of a careful and liberal management'.[36]

Henry Parsey makes no comment regarding the presence or absence of animals within the Hatton asylum in his diary or in any of his annual reports, although in 1876 he did report to the Visitors:

> Miss Raynes [Matron] seconds my endeavours to preserve to the Asylum a tone of domesticity which, unless vigilantly cultured, is apt to be lost and to degenerate with increase in number into a cold and impersonal regime.

By inference it might be assumed that such domesticity

would include flowers and pet birds (and possibly other animals) within the asylum, but confirmation only comes from an article in the Leamington Spa Courier of 7 September 1871 on the occasion of the opening of the Idiot Asylum 'quietly and without any demonstration', which provided a guided tour of the new building for its readers:

> *[The day rooms] are neatly furnished, and supplied with various amusements such as draughts, dominoes, fox and geese and bagatelle. Flowers ornament the various windows, and pet birds at least [sic] appeared to be tolerated as pets.*

Quite so: they were fashionable and added colour and birdsong to routine daily lives, and offered some responsibility as carers to the more capable inmates.

THE ASYLUM EXPANDS

Henry Parsey's regime within the Asylum was all very laudable, of course, if somewhat limited therapeutically: but then, as we have seen, the nineteenth century alienists did not possess a pharmacological armamentarium against mental illness apart from opiates, used mainly as a sedative for the more acutely manic or floridly deluded patients, and aperients to ensure regularity of bowel function (which Conolly considered essential in any well-ordered institution, and of course, it was a universally Victorian preoccupation).

By the mid-nineteenth Century, the application of leeches, purgation and annual bleeding in the springtime – which had been very much a feature of treatment in Bethlem Hospital for many years – had fallen into disrepute, being associated with the ancient Greek theory that all mortal ills resulted from of an imbalance between the four humours (black bile, yellow bile, phlegm and blood), which blood-letting and purgation would (somehow) restore.[37] Samuel Tuke's 'Description of the Retreat' had documented the lack of efficacy of the then routine administration of medications to purge, vomit, or sedate, which were then abandoned, so that pharmacological treatments were very infrequently administered (apart from aperients) until the mid 1880s, when the sedative chloral hydrate came into common use; this is surprising when one considers the range and amount of medications, (mostly morphine and laudanum based, but not excluding toxic heavy metals such as arsenic and antimony), which were dispensed by chemists and consumed avidly (too avidly, some might say) by the Victorian middle classes.

Indeed, in his annual report of 1856, quoted earier, Dr Parsey had commented that medication was used as a treatment of the insane 'in the restricted sense'.

Ever the optimist, Dr Parsey was always urging in his reports the prompt admission of lunatics into the Asylum: it was generally considered paramount by alienists of the day that early intervention in mental illness, (which of necessity required the removal of the patient into the asylum) would offer a greater prospect of cure than presentation when illness was well established. The common practice of caring for lunatics at home, however laudable, or the tardy referral from the Union houses, for financial reasons, was to be regretted.

Most of Dr Parsey's annual reports would contain a comment such as the one below:

This Asylum is still regarded too much as a mere receptacle for the cases of mental disorder and decay, too inconvenient or troublesome to be longer treated in their homes or Union houses, instead of an

Institution specially adapted to the care and treatment of insanity in its earlier and more curable stages.

Admirably, the Warwick Union sent its insane poor to the Asylum, 'as soon as their mental condition came under the cognizance of its relieving officers' but most did not; (there was, of course, a legal requirement under the 1845 Lunacy Act to do this within 14 days of admission, as we know, but by many Union houses this was honoured more in the breach than the observance).

He went on to state:

> *It is a common remark of strangers, that a large proportion of the inmates appear perfectly quiet and inoffensive; and it is to many a subject of surprise that their detention is considered necessary: and that they cannot be equally well taken care of in the Union houses or by their families or friends.*
>
> *Many of the patients who have been sent to the Asylum because they have become quite unmanageable, to the experienced observer, present the most striking examples of the beneficial effects of the present treatment of insanity as practiced in this Asylum.*[38]

Dr Parsey, a self-confessed disciple of Conolly and Bucknill, would have considered this an ever-present concern; the condition was known as 'asylum cure': whilst the patient may seem docile and *compos mentis* within the daily regime of the asylum, to assume a 'cure' and to therefore discharge the patient from the asylum, to 'family care' at best, or the workhouse, where there was no provision at all for continued care, would inevitably result in relapse.

In 1860 the introduction of a Free Trade agreement with France resulted in cheap French ribbon flooding the domestic market. The industry had provided work for

30,000 weavers (half the population of Coventry) who mainly worked from home as out-workers, and the effect of the foreign imports was catastrophic. Coventry's ribbon-weaving industry collapsed and many thousands of workers and their families were left destitute. Although there were a considerable number of admissions to the asylum during Dr Parsey's years of patients professing to be weavers (see Appendix 6), Dr Parsey commented in his 1861 report:

The great and continued distress among the weaving population of Coventry and its immediate neighbourhood might have been expected to add somewhat to our numbers in the past year but the distress, great as it has been, does not appear to have led to any increase of mental disorder.

Likewise, whilst there were also quite a number of watchmakers admitted to the asylum, this too was probably in proportion to the number of watchmakers in Coventry at the time (but this industry also collapsed at the end of the century, this time due to cheap American imports).

But the inexorable rise in numbers admitted to the asylum, and the comparative lack of cure disappointed Dr Parsey; after the asylum had been open for a decade it accommodated 368 patients – considerably more than the asylum had been built to provide for. Dr Parsey was becoming just a little agitated:

The numbers in the Asylum now are considerably above those contemplated in the original design of the buildings and press closely on the extreme amount of accommodation that has been made available only by various adaptations and internal re-arrangements.[39]

The Commissioners in Lunacy in London tried to pour oil on troubled waters:

The crazy imbecile who, 500 years ago, would have roamed the hamlet, or the fields, is now protected within the asylum, tranquil, occupied, self-respecting and happy. A great accumulation of chronic lunatics in asylums ought not to cause surprise by its amount, nor complaint on account of its expense.[40]

But relief was to come from an unexpected quarter.

★

As we have seen, Henry Parsey and the Committee of Visitors had followed Conolly's precepts for the successful running of an asylum in the age of 'moral management', by appointing a chaplain when the asylum first opened. A chapel had been built, with a fine hammerbeam roof (architectural drawings in the asylum archive confirm this). Conolly had been enthusiastic about chapel attendance – he thought that insane persons were capable of deriving much satisfaction from being permitted to attend the services of their church, and observed:

Those who have never been in the chapel of an asylum are generally surprised to find that the patients join in the responses and the singing, in a manner which some sane congregations would do well to imitate.[41]

The chapel soon proved to be inadequate to accommodate the increasing numbers. In 1863, Dr Parsey informed the Visitors that:

The numbers in the asylum are now considerably above those contemplated in the original design of the buildings and press closely on the extreme amount of accommodation that has been made available by various adaptations and internal re-arrangements.

Of all the alterations and improvements of the past year, there has been none to bear any comparison with the useful comfort, and really necessary additional accommodation, afforded by the erection of a new and commodious Chapel. Our old chapel had become altogether too small for the patients likely to be able to attend Divine Service out of the number the asylum now holds, as was manifested by the fact that on the opening of the new one about 40 more were present than could be in any way be found room for previously. There is also now proper space and accommodation for those of the out-door servants whose family live in the Asylum grounds, and who previously were unprovided for.

The new Chapel had consequently become in itself a necessity; but by its erection other pressing wants for additional space have been conveniently and satisfactorily met.

Our room for general amusements had always been very small and ill-adapted for its purpose; but by converting to this use the old Chapel, a large room, 42 x 32 feet, we have now a spacious and very convenient recreation room.

And this adaptation has enabled you [the Committee of Visitors] to meet a further want that the increasing size of the Asylum was causing to be urgently felt, that of an appropriate place in which the patient could be visited by their relatives.

Until quite lately we had as visiting rooms only two small, badly-lit rooms at the back of the entrance hall, which are applied to the additional purpose of receiving rooms for the new patients on their admission, whilst the necessary preliminaries to their being sent to one of the wards are being gone through. This was an occasional source of extreme inconvenience, when a new patient was presented for admission on the usual visiting days for the patients' friends. We are now able to use the old recreation room partly for its former purposes as an appendage to the newly-acquired one, but chiefly as the place of meeting for patients and their friends, much to the satisfaction of all of them.'

Thus a new chapel – hardly a building which the Visitors could

cavil about on the grounds of expense – proved to be the means
of reducing overcrowding in the asylum generally.

ASYLUM CARE FOR NON-PAUPERS

The asylum had begun admitting fee-paying patients (at a
surcharge of two shillings per week on the pauper rate) in
1858, but this ceased in 1864; presumably because the capacity
of the Asylum was becoming overstretched by providing
accommodation for these additional patients, given the
numbers of paupers being admitted. Dr Parsey confirms this
suspicion in his report to the Visitors of the previous year:

> *In this county it is to the extended facilities afforded to those not really
> paupers, by arrangements with the parochial authorities, for obtaining
> shelter within our walls that much of the unexpected increase in
> our numbers is to be attributed. It should be borne in mind that the
> reception into the asylum of such cases was not originally contemplated,
> and that the presence not merely swells the apparent number of pauper
> lunatics, but from the publicity given to our statistics tends to foster the
> alarm which is now getting strong possession of the public mind that
> there is a rapid increase of lunacy amongst us.*

Provision for care of lunatics from the lower middle classes
was a very great problem: whilst that class were not paupers
per se, neither had they sufficient monies to contemplate
private asylum or 'madhouse' care. Dr Parsey was very
concerned about this dilemma indeed:

> *That asylums, in which the insane from the classes removed from
> above the absolute poor can be received and properly treated, at a
> comparatively trifling cost, are very urgently needed must be patent to
> all who give even a cursory thought to this subject.*

> *That such asylums should be entirely independent of the existing county ones, there are many valid reasons for desiring; and that, could they be brought into existence, the present County Asylums would be greatly relieved of the pressure for room that is experienced in all of them, is very certain.*
>
> *The difficulty, however, of accompanying so desirable and useful a work will be so great as to be almost insurmountable until the absolute need of them becomes much more generally felt and understood than it is at present. The few asylums of a somewhat similar character that have sprung up in the last few years have their scale of charges so high as to practically entirely to exclude those members of the community that so really require the shelter they might have afforded.*
>
> *Bethlehem and St Luke's Hospitals in London are still the only two which address themselves especially to the mitigation of this want, and unfortunately, so little publicity is given to the advantages they are able to offer, that their very existence as charitable institutions for the insane from among the lower of the middle classes, much less the admirable manner in which they are conducted, is scarcely known in those quarters in which the benefits they can confer might be taken advantage of and converted into really so many blessings.*[42]

The existing arrangement in England of admitting the lower middle classes to County Asylums, with relatives and Parishes sharing the expense was unsatisfactory; it caused additional expense on the Poor Rate, an additional burden on providing asylum accommodation and also 'social degradation' in those admitted. He suggested a plan to provide asylums for the lower middle classes by subscription to provide non-profit treatment, but provision of such premises continued to be very limited throughout the century, and remained a very great source of anxiety to the middle classes.

This was the first year that a new suggestion to reduce numbers in the main asylum was mooted:

Forty patients belong to the class denominated idiots; if it should at some time be necessary to enlarge the asylum, it would be a question whether it will not be advisable to provide separate accommodation for this class.

Victorian prose style is tiring to read and a hindrance to understanding exactly what he is trying to say, but I think the suggestion seems to be a sensible one, in principle, and followed orthodox alienist thinking at the time.

RELEASE FROM THE ASYLUM

'Proper persons to be admitted' to the asylum had no right of appeal, under the 1845 Act. Relatives or friends might request a patient's discharge from the asylum, but the final decision rested with the Committee of Visitors – on the Medical Superintendent's recommendation, or by edict of the Commissioners in Lunacy in London.

Three patients have been discharged to the care of their relatives, who have given the necessary legal guarantee that they shall be properly cared for, and not again be chargeable to a Parish or Union. Applications from the friends of other patients for their discharge in a similar way have been made to your committee; but the advance towards recovery, if any, was in none of them sufficiently marked to have allowed their removal from an Asylum without much chance of eventual mishap either to themselves or to others; and though their individual friends may have felt aggrieved at your exercising the power, allowed by law, of refusing their application, the ratepayers of the Union, that would have been supposed to be relieved of their charge, must be more satisfied to contribute to the maintenance of a dangerous lunatic, than to hear that he is handed over, at certain hazard to the community, to the doubtful care and keeping of some

poor relative, who tenders a guarantee that there is no reasonable
probability of his being able to carry out.[43]

ASSISTANCE

Conolly had written in his book 'On the Construction and
Government of Lunatic Asylums and other Hospitals for
the Insane', in 1857:

The duty of seeing every patient twice, or even once a day, prescribing
for those who are sick, listening to the representations and complaints of
others, giving direction for the special attentions required in particular
cases, ascertaining that nothing important is omitted in the diet, clothing,
exercise, classification, examining new patients, keeping records and
registers of cases, and attending to all the applications incidental to is
office, becomes extremely laborious for one medical officer, when the
patients exceed 300 in number. [44]

The asylum Visitors must have been quite enlightened, for
in 1857, Dr Parsey thanked them for granting him a part-
time Medical Assistant (at £450pa, with board and lodging),
'affording him relief from duties which though they occupy
much time, could be easily delegated to a junior'.

His first Assistant was Wardle Bowen, who was to
remain in post until 1864. Wardle Bowen was the only son
of Frederick Bowen of Harrow, Middlesex, who styled
himself 'Surgeon' in the 1851 census. Frederick Bowen
held the double qualification of Licentiate of Apothecaries
Hall and Membership of the Royal College of Surgeons
– 'College and Hall' – and was a 'surgeon apothecary'; in
essence, a general practitioner. Wardle, born in Harrow
in 1834, also became a Member of the Royal College of
Surgeons, obtaining Membership in 1855 and joined the

Asylum staff in 1858 as Medical Assistant. Presumably he thought his career lay outside general practice, and so did not pursue the LSA diploma.

Dr Parsey would have a succession of assistants for the rest of his career: they stayed in post for a variable number of years whilst gaining clinical experience at the asylum, before moving on to take up Medical Superintendent positions in other asylums, or enter private practice, sometimes as proprietors of their own asylums or 'licensed houses', as Conolly had done on leaving Hanwell.

TEMPTATION

In 1860, a former patient of the Public Lunatic Asylum in Kingston, Jamaica, had published allegations of abuses she suffered and the appalling conditions she endured during her admission to the asylum, in a pamphlet entitled 'Seven Months in the Kingston Lunatic Asylum and What I Saw There'.[45] It caused a scandal, and a Government Inquiry found that there had indeed been much abuse of patients over the years, which Matron and her nurses had apparently managed to hide from the doctors and other senior staff, and also that there was also an unacceptably high level of disease and mortality within the asylum. Conolly was aware of this pattern of behaviour: in 1847 he had written:

> The Matron of an asylum is usually chosen by the governing body; but it is a great evil in an asylum when this officer is made of too much importance, and led to consider herself independent of the physician [...] I am very sorry to say it, but in the generality of examinations made, or inquests held, in hospitals or workhouses, or asylums, the matrons do not appear to advantage, and are often found to be the most

effective agents for harsh purposes. There is reason to believe, also, that in some asylums in which mechanical restraints are yet employed, their abolition has been prevented by the matron.

Matron and two nurses were dismissed from their posts, as were the Chief Medical Officer and his assistant.

The Government Inquiry revealed that 'moral management', by now universal practice throughout England and Wales, did not feature in the Kingston Asylum, and the regime of care of inmates was still very much that of containment, physical restraint and abuse, and it was recommended that the new Medical Superintendent should be an experienced British alienist.

In the asylum's archive there is a letter from Dr Parsey's grandson, Edward Moreland Parsey, written by hand on 15 April 1952, addressed to Dr Edward Stern, the then Medical Director at the asylum (by then renamed the Central Hospital), and received by him during preparations for its Centenary celebrations in 1952. The letter contains, among other biographical details of his grandfather, the following passage:

In 1860 he was offered a most important and lucrative Colonial appointment in his own specialty, couched in the most flattering terms, which in consequence of his deep interest in the Asylum which he had organized from its commencement, he refused.

A few years later he was offered a Commissionership in Lunacy, which he refused for the same reasons as those referred to above.

It seems most likely that the new Medical Superintendent post in Kingston, Jamaica, was that which Dr Parsey had been offered and declined. In the event, Dr Thomas Allen, Medical Superintendent of the Lincolnshire County Lunatic Asylum took up the position in 1863.

Clearly, Dr Parsey's initial unsettledness, manifested by his repeated applications in the early years after his arrival at Hatton for other Medical Superintendent posts around the country, had resolved.

★

In 1860, a new Chaplain, Rev Thomas Bourne Dickins, Vicar of All Saints Church, Emscote, replaced Mr Gurden, who had been Chaplain since Dr Wood's resignation and departure for Canada. Dr Parsey said of the Rev Gurden on his departure:

He has by his kind feeling, good judgment and ready sympathy […] awakened sentiments of respect and affection for himself, which will long be cherished by many, who will probably never in this life pass permanently beyond the precincts of this asylum.

He then introduced his successor, the Rev Dickins, to the Visitors:

In his successor we have a Chaplain highly esteemed and valued as a parochial clergyman and who enters into the spirit of the somewhat more peculiar charge devolving on him here.

The Rev Dickins, Vicar of All Saints Church, Emscote, was to become a long-standing colleague and friend to Dr Parsey and his family over the years, and continued to be Chaplain to the Asylum until he retired in 1888, at which point his son, the Rev Richard Dickins, succeeded him as Chaplain (and also as Vicar of All Saints).

Perhaps the Asylum was now more settled generally; the most recent Matron, the fourth in the Asylum's history, had been in post for four years; (presumed) personality clashes had resolved and Dr Parsey had an assistant to help with the more mundane medical duties of the Asylum.

★

Domestically, however, during this period, life was not so settled for the Parseys: after their first child, Julia Mary ('Julie'), had been born on 15 May 1853, they were to suffer the loss in infancy or childhood of their next three children in rapid succession. In 1855, their second daughter Helen Louisa died from 'haemorrhage', aged eleven days; in 1859, their third daughter Ada Elizabeth died from 'dropsey', aged two years; and in 1862, their first son William George died from 'dental irritation and cerebral effusion', also aged two years.

The three children had all been baptized in Hatton church; Helen Louisa and Amy Elizabeth by the incumbent at Hatton at the time, but William George was baptized by Rev Lovell Procter, Julia Parsey's brother.

According to the burial register, all three children were buried in the churchyard of Hatton church, but only William George is commemorated on Henry Parsey's tomb.

Their last child, Edward William, was born in 1864. Julie and he both survived into old age. Julie never married and was 'of independent means'; Edward William qualified in medicine from Cambridge and St Thomas's, married, and had a long career in general practice in King's Norton, then a small village on the outskirts of Birmingham.

★

In 1863, Henry Parsey stated in his report, that:

it is with much satisfaction and thankfulness that I am able to report

*that in the 10½ years that the Asylum has been open I have not had to
report the occurrence of a suicide.*

Patients with suicidal propensities were treated on the
principle of:

*not leading them to suppose that they are objects of more than ordinary
attention; by keeping them as much as practicable within sight and
mixed with the other patients in the daytime; and at night placing them
in associated dormitories where there are some other patients of sufficient
intelligence and inclination to call the night attendant if necessary.*

When suicidal patients were considered unfit for 'associated
dormitories', the other precautions of a single bedroom –
with regular observation – or the padded room and 'clothing
that cannot be well-used for self-destruction' were resorted
to; likewise for those at risk of injuring others.

Just under 40% of both male and female patients
admitted to Hatton during its first year of operation were
'at risk' of suicide or 'dangerous to others', according to
their Orders of Admission (with a slightly higher number
of males being considered to be 'dangerous to others', as
one would expect).[46]

It was orthodox medical opinion that the mild
regimentation of day-to-day life in the asylum and the
competence of the attendants would prove a calming
influence, and indeed, in most asylums suicide was
uncommon; 'opportunity is almost always the parent
of impulse', wrote Dr Parsey, so that with the standard
asylum regime of uninterrupted supervision of potential
suicidees, a five or seven year gap between successful
attempts was about the average frequency in asylums in
England. Be that as it may, there will always remain those
who are driven to such a course of action. None who work

with the mentally ill can ever be complacent that a suicide will not occur.

So, after eleven years of operation, the inevitable did occur within the asylum, but from an unexpected quarter.

Dr Parsey's assistant Wardle Bowen appears to have carried out his duties conscientiously during the six years he was resident in the Asylum. The Annual Report of 1864 had stated:

Both Mr Bowen[47] and myself have endeavoured to provide faithfully such professional assistance as in our judgement we have considered advisable.

But, with much gravitas, Dr Parsey informed the Visitors the following year that:

Among the incidents of the past year there is one very painful in its circumstance [...] which was the removal from us, by a melancholy and sudden death, of Mr Wardle Bowen who had for six years occupied in the post of Assistant Medical Officer here; and who, by the cheerfulness and kindliness of his disposition, and the active personal interest he took in all that conduced to the comfort and happiness of the inmates [sic], had made himself a great favourite among them. The suddenness of his removal from a state of apparent perfect health, exerted a very depressing influence over several of the patients, demanding for some time afterwards much anxious care to guard against such untoward circumstances as might be likely to arise from the morbid suggestions of a community constituted as ours is.

It was a very great surprise, therefore, to discover from Wardle Bowen's death certificate that he had died not from an acute major illness for which the Victorians had no remedy, but that he had committed suicide in the asylum 'by swallowing prussic acid [cyanide] while in a state of temporary insanity', according to the findings of a Coroner's inquest held the following day.

A slightly lugubrious report of the inquest was reported in the Royal Leamington Spa Courier on 23 April 1864:

MELANCHOLY SUICIDE AT THE HATTON ASYLUM –
On Wednesday morning Mr Wardle Bowen, who for the past six years has been acting in the capacity of assistant medical officer at the Hatton Lunatic Asylum, was found dead in his bedroom by one of the attendants of the institution. The deceased gentleman came from Harrow, and was only 20 years of age [he was in fact aged 30]. An inquest was held at the Asylum on Thursday evening, before Mr W.S. Poole, coroner, and a respectable jury. From the evidence of Dr Parsey it appeared that deceased had an interview with him on Wednesday morning, and on its conclusion Dr Parsey left him to go to chapel. Soon afterwards he was informed that Mr Bowen was dead in his bedroom. He immediately hastened there, when he found the deceased lying on the floor on his face. He saw an empty bottle in the room, which had contained prussic acid, and he at once applied the usual remedies to procure animation, but without success, life having been extinct for some minutes. Both Dr Parsey and the Rev T. R. Dickins, the chaplain to the Asylum, bore their testimony to the recent altered mental condition of the deceased, and added that he occasionally shewed morbid excitement and depression of spirits, which is supposed to have been caused by some troubles of a private character. Dr Parsey feeling, under the circumstances, that he ought not to make a post mortem examination of the body, Dr Tibbits, at the request of the coroner did so. On examining the stomach, he at once found that the immediate cause of death was the presence of prussic acid in it. The jury returned a verdict that deceased died from the effects of prussic acid taken while in a state of temporary insanity.

'It was highly regrettable that a young man's medical career – and indeed his brief life – should have ended so tragically', remarked Dr Parsey. Quite so, and it is pointless

Portrait photograph of Dr Henry Parsey (1821 – 1884).

The first 'Warwick County Asylum' at Stretton-on-Dunsmore.

Memorial to Sir Joseph Paxton in the London Road Cemetery, Coventry.

Front view of the main entrance to the asylum today.

Stratford-upon-Avon's first Dispensary.

Warwick's first Dispensary.

Silver salver presented by the Mayor of Stratford-upon-Avon
to Dr John Conolly.

Silver Testimonial presented to Dr John Conolly.

Bronze bust of Dr John Conolly.

Tomb of Sir John Bucknill at Clifton-on Dunsmore, Warwickshire.

Architect's drawing of the proposed 'Warneford General Bathing Institution and Leamington Hospital'.

Warneford Medal awarded to Henry Parsey by King's College, University of London (June 1838).

Dr Parsey's carriage outside the main entrance to the asylum.

ALL GLORY BE TO GOD THERE SHALL BE NO MORE
DEATH / WILLIAM HENRY PARSEY MD WHO FELL ASLEEP
/ ON THE 10TH OF JANUARY 1884 ALSO JULIA HIS WIFE /
ON THE 9TH DAY OF JULY 1896 JULIA MARY THEIR ONLY
/ DAUGHTER HAS PLACED THIS WINDOW TO THEIR /
MEMORY EASTER 1898 RESURGEMUS

Memorial window in Holy Trinity Church, Hatton.

Photograph of Dr Alfred Miller MB, Medical Superintendent of the Hatton asylum from 1891-1923.

Wooden panel in memory of Dr Alfred Miller.

to speculate on the content of Wardle Bowen's interview with Dr Parsey, and what influence it had had – if any – on his subsequent course of action.

The first suicide amongst the patients two years later was an equally distressing event; in his annual report of 1866, Dr Parsey gave details of a female patient who:

had escaped the building, and who then successfully set fire to her clothing, deliberately and with the exercise of much precaution, to ensure the accomplishment of her object, and subsequently died.

At the inquest the Coroner and jury were unanimous in the expression of an opinion, exonerating her special attendants, or anyone else connected with the Asylum, from blame or the charge of carelessness. This opinion was endorsed by the relatives of the deceased present at the inquest, as also by your Committee.[48]

The next suicide in the Asylum occurred some seven years later; Dr Parsey commented in his 1873 Annual Report that:

the good fortune that has for so long a time attended this asylum in its freedom from suicides has failed in this present year.

A female patient, resident 2½ years, but with determined suicidal tendencies, escaped from an airing court and then drowned in the canal.

And fast upon the heels of this second suicide of a patient came a second suicide of a member of staff: on 5 February 1875 an inquest was held in the asylum on Edward Bytheway, aged thirty two, formerly a butcher from Bridgnorth, but for the past two years an attendant at the Asylum.

Apparently, on the morning of 3 February the deceased

was discovered in his bedroom at 6.30am, not having appeared for duties, with his throat cut. The previous evening he had complained of feeling unwell and retired to bed at 8.45pm. Dr Woods, the Assistant Medical Officer, said that when found the deceased had been dead for 3-4 hours. An open verdict was delivered.[49]

This proved to be the last suicide during Dr Parsey's lifetime, but during this period of time one patient escaped from the asylum. Robert Seel escaped during an entertainment for the patients, which Seel and others in his ward had declined to attend. Seel somehow escaped from the locked ward whilst the ward attendant was otherwise engaged but was met in the yard outside his ward by the sub-engineer. Seel managed to overpower the sub-engineer and escape in the dark. He was described in the newspapers as 'deluded and thinks he is the rightful heir to the King of England and talks of being worth millions'.

He was apprehended shortly afterwards in the neighborhood, and was returned to the asylum. This was normal procedure.

If, however, patients were able to make their escape and remain at large for fourteen days or longer, then a new Order for Admission was required by the Asylum Superintendent (under the Lunacy Acts) before re-admission could be effected.

The late 1860s became a period of preoccupation with the building of the new Idiot Asylum, as we shall see in the next chapter, but meanwhile day-to-day affairs of the main asylum with the ever-increasing number of patients continued to occupy Dr Parsey's daily life.

ENDNOTES

1. The Director of Music from 1946-1992 was Martindale

Sidwell, b Little Packington. He was previously Director of Music at Warwick School and organist at Holy Trinity Church, Leamington Spa.

2. George Frideric Handel (1685-1759), composer of *Messiah*, who lived in Brook Street for many years, was a worshipper there.

3. Church of St John the Baptist, Wolvey, Warwickshire.

4. The Hospital moved to its present site in Denmark Hill in 1913.

5. A guinea = '£1 and one shilling' (£1.05p) and was the currency of professional fees; a guinea then would be equivalent to at least £100 today.

6. As ever; note James Joyce's observation regarding Dublin medical students: 'Trinity medicals ... all prick and no pence'; *Ulysses* Penguin, London (2000) p427.

7. Over £80,000 today.

8. Josiah Clarkson *Warneford Prize Essay 1843*.

9. The Warneford Medals were made from bronze by Joseph & Alfred Wyon, of Portland Place, London. The Wyon family were eminent engravers and medallists and Joseph and Alfred were both appointed Chief Engraver of the Seals, as had been their father Benjamin before them.

10. It appears that this is a correct assumption: Warwick University Medical School awards an annual undergraduate 'Dr Henry Parsey Psychiatry Prize' (endowed by the Coventry & Warwickshire NHS Trust).

11. Rivington *The Medical Profession*.

12. Parry-Jones *Trade in Lunacy* p238-9.

13. After the introduction of the Medical Register, the LSA was considered to be an inferior qualification and a dubious route to Registration; it was known disparagingly as the 'License to Slay Anybody'.

14. At that time the MD was awarded by examination rather than by thesis.

15. *Report of the Commissioners in Lunacy 1862*.

16. *Report of the Commissioners in Lunacy 1893*.

17. Visit by John Conolly to the Hatton Asylum 1856.

18. For further details see Appendix 6.

19. An asylum in Bethnal Green owned by Thomas Warburton. Used by parishes in London and the Home Counties to accommodate their lunatics when there was no local facility. It had had in earlier times a fearsome reputation, but by the middle of the 19C. was a model of mental health care.

20. WHP *Annual Report 1864*.

21. WHP *Annual Report 1853*.

22. Which could only be signed by 'a Fellow or Licentiate of the Royal College of Physicians of London or a graduate in medicine of a University [to be stated on the certificate] or a Member of the Royal College of Surgeons in London or an Apothecary duly authorized to practice by the Apothecaries Company in London'. This was before the General Medical Register came into being in 1868.

23. In 1860 he was appointed a Medical Officer to the Midland County Asylum at Knowle.

24. The Warwick House of Correction or Bridewell (demolished 1972) stood at the corner of Theatre Street and Barrack Street, and accommodated over 200 minor offenders, beggars and vagrants sentenced to hard labour in the flour mill (men) or in the kitchen (women). After 1860 they were sent to the new gaol in Cape Road (demolished, apart from the Governor's House, in 1934).

25. Annual Report of the Commissioners in Lunacy, reported in *Royal Leamington Spa Courier* 8 January 1881.

26. Clark *Memoir of John Conolly* p29

27. 'Menorrhagia' is defined as 'prolonged and excessive menstrual bleeding': this seems appropriate, for her history of physical illness was of chronic blood loss from heavy periods and haemorrhoids ('piles'); attempts at correcting this with oral haematinics (agents required for blood formation eg iron, folic acid etc) were thwarted by her refusal to take any form of medication. Blood transfusion was not an option until the 1920s.

28. Another TCD graduate, q 1872, who became MS of the Somerset and Bath Asylum, Wells.
29. *Parliamentary Papers 1842* XIX pp 42-43.
30. From *'Jemima'* by Henry Wadsworth Longfellow (1807-1882). American poet.
31. *Royal Leamington Spa Courier* 4 June 1881 & 11 June 1881.
32. A photograph from the late 1890s of the inmates and staff of the Doncaster workhouse in South Yorkshire includes 'the no doubt much-loved workhouse dog, held in the arms of the porter'. May *The Victorian Workhouse.*
33. Allderidge 'A cat, surpassing in beauty, and other therapeutic animals' *Psych Bulletin* (1991), 15, 759-62.
34. Conolly *Construction of Lunatic Asylums* p55.
35. Ibid.
36. Annual Report of the Committee of Visitors 1855.
37. This theory had influenced European medicine since the age of Hippocrates until about the middle of the C.18th
38. WHP *Annual Report 1860.*
39. WHP *Annual Report 1863.*
40. *Annual Report of the Committee of Visitors 1855.*
41. Conolly *Construction of Lunatic Asylums* p125.
42. WHP *Annual Report 1864.*
43. WHP *Annual Report 1864.*
44. Conolly *Construction of Lunatic Asylums.*
45. Pratt *Seven Months in the Kingston Lunatic Asylum.*
46. Of 66 females admitted, 21 were 'suicidal' and 5 'dangerous to others', of 74 males admitted the numbers were 19 and 10.
47. Titled 'Mr' Bowen because he was merely MRCS – a qualification in surgery.
48. WHP *Annual Report 1866.*
49. *Royal Leamington Spa Courier* 13 February 1875.

CHAPTER 5

THE ADDITION OF 'HIGHFIELD', AN ASYLUM FOR IDIOTS

In the Annual Report of 1863, Dr Parsey made his usual preamble regarding overcrowding within the asylum, then emphasized the proportion of idiots accommodated and his preferred solution:

> *Present numbers are 401(181 males & 220 females). Of this number 40 patients belong to the class denominated Idiots; and if it should be at some future time be necessary to enlarge the Asylum, it will be a question whether it will not be advisable to provide separate accommodation for this class.*

In 1866, now with sixty idiots in the asylum (and the certainty of more in future years), Dr Parsey advised the Committee of Visitors that:

> *In the asylum there are 39 male and 21 female idiots and imbeciles; some of these under 10 years of age.*

The asylum has existed for 16 years, built originally to accommodate 325 patients; it has been made capable by additions and alterations of containing 463.

His opinion was that:

any such general alterations to the buildings of the present asylum will involve (for the laundry, bakehouse and offices generally would need alteration or replacement) an outlay probably as great or greater than would be required for an entirely new building of unpretentious character complete in itself and properly adapted to the requirements of idiots.

The Committee duly deliberated and proposed that 'a separate asylum should be provided for present and future idiots', because the main asylum which provided accommodation – but little else – for them, meant they were 'almost without any hope of their condition being ameliorated'.

Plainly, the desire to improve the lot of patients by instruction in such an asylum and in such a manner was an expression of 'moral management' at its best, producing recognisable improvements in behaviour in general and 'perceptible improvement of the mental faculties of some of those engaged in them'.

In July 1868, the Committee decided that land adjacent to the main asylum was the most suitable site and architects were approached to prepare a plan and estimate for a building capable of accommodating two hundred patients with kitchen, offices and outbuildings.

In January 1869 designs for the proposed buildings were eventually sanctioned, after the Commissioners in Lunacy in London had added their recommendations, as committees do, which required alterations and additions – and added expense – to the plans submitted.

The design now accommodated two hundred residents, the sexes segregated in identical wings which included day rooms and a school room, with a central dining room, kitchen and stores etc., (including a basement and 'ale and beer store'), and with additional accommodation for staff – which was sorely needed – at a total cost of £10,000.

Building commenced in April 1869, and a building whose bricks matched those of the main asylum, once again being made from clay within the grounds, began to appear. An additional Assistant Medical Officer, Dr Oliver Woods, a TCD graduate and Licenciate of the Royal College of Surgeons in Ireland,[1] was appointed with specific responsibility for the new asylum, and eventually, with a staff of nine attendants and one night nurse, the doors opened for the reception of patients in August 1871.

The Leamington Spa Courier wrote gushingly of the new Asylum in its edition of 7 September 1871:

> *The structure consists of two extensive wings with a west frontage, divided from each other by an entrance hall. The new institution stands on an elevated piece of land, commanding a magnificent view of the surrounding country, from the Shuckburgh hills on the east, to those of Brailes on the west, and extending across the Feldon of Warwickshire, to historic Edgehill.*

★

The United Kingdom, for all its merits in the care it provided for lunatics in the nineteenth century, lagged behind the Continent somewhat in its provision of institutions for idiots.

The first asylum for idiots in England had been established in Highgate, which opened in 1848. It soon proved to be too small, and so Earlswood Asylum was built near Redhill, in Surrey, which opened in 1855. Conolly had been involved with both. Earlswood accommodated five hundred residents, mostly from the middle and upper classes, who paid private fees but some 'deserving poor' had their fees paid by subscribers to the institution. The first Medical Superintendent was Dr John Langdon Down (of

124

'Down's syndrome' fame).[2] Soon, other similar institutions followed.

Whilst at Hanwell, Conolly had been to France to visit the Salpetrière Hospital (an institution of 1600 insane women) to see the schooling conducted there, which had appropriated techniques used in France in communicating with the deaf and dumb.

He became enthused, and instituted schooling in reading, writing, drawing and singing for many of the patients at Hanwell, and was gratified with the improvements in literacy and general behaviour which resulted. For reasons unknown, schooling of the patients in Hanwell was suppressed 'by an authority which I had no power of resisting' wrote Conolly – presumably the Governors of the asylum. But this did not curb his enthusiasm; he helped to establish the idiot asylum in Highgate and maintained that:

> *if few cases admit of cure, every case admits of improvement; if no other end were answered by the formation of schools, they ought to be established as recreative, palliative, remedial even, in every lunatic asylum.*[3]

John Bucknill had done exactly that at Exminster: he arranged 'evening-school classes' which consisted of reading, writing and arithmetic lessons in several of the wards, under the supervision of an experienced schoolmaster and carried out by the attendants. He wrote likewise that 'their influence as a source of wholesome mental occupation has been entirely beneficial'.

Without doubt, Henry Parsey would have had experience of these classes at Exminster during his assistantship years there.

★

125

The Warwick County Idiot Asylum was not, however, the first asylum for idiots in the County. A small asylum 'for the education and training of idiots and imbeciles' had been established in Knowle in 1868. A new building was commenced in 1872, following a fanfare of publicity regarding the laying of the foundation stone, which included – inexplicably – the use of the same mallet as Charles II had used to lay the foundation stone of St Paul's Cathedral. There was a great deal of national newspaper coverage of the event.

This asylum was a very small venture, however, with accommodation for only twenty children at any one time. It admitted children from all the Midland counties, funded partly by the counties and also by a fee-paying policy for each admission, and was therefore available only to the middle classes. It gained a reputation for a surprisingly successful improvement in behaviour of its charges, and no doubt followed the same principles that Dr Parsey would adopt in the Idiot Asylum at Hatton.[4]

★

Dr Parsey had initially not been very enthusiastic regarding schooling for the idiots and imbeciles, because they presented to the asylum 'usually well past youth', and their prospects for education were poor, but he became less pessimistic with the passage of time, and suggested to the Visitors that, with schooling, their day-to-day care would be less onerous for the attendants, and that some patients might, in time, become able to perform menial tasks within the asylum that assisted its day-to-day running, but did not consider that their intellect could be trained to such a capacity that they would be able to return to their homes, where they could be economically useful in the household. He was ever the realist. In 1862 he had stated:

*All I wish to impress is, the education of idiots should be taken for what
it is worth, and not made the foundation for a superstructure of vain
hopes of intellectual advancement out of the ranks of an asylum into the
busy ranks of everyday life.*[5]

After a year, fifty males and thirty three females had been
transferred from the main asylum to the new Idiot Asylum, by
then known as 'Highfield', together with 'some of the more
inoffensive of the chronic insane, who by their example and
capabilities for instruction exercise a beneficial influence'.

He was able to report that at the end of the second year
of Highfield's operation, of the ninety one residents, half
were receiving school instruction and about three-quarters
were capable of some form of employment; in the laundry,
knitting and sewing, (quite skilled tasks, surely), in 'simple
trades' and 'running messages', (again, quite a responsible
task).

The school instruction classes provided at Highfield
for the idiots differed from those that had been provided
a generation previously by Conolly and Bucknill. The
teaching of 'clock lesson' (teaching the hours, quarters and
minutes, including 'telling the time to a minute'); 'shop
lesson' (knowing coins and weights, even to 'knowing
coins and weights and calculating fairly') and 'colour lesson'
(knowing black and white and colours and 'being able to
match most sample colours and shades') appears to be
setting quite a high standard of education.

By 1875, Highfield contained one hundred and four
idiots, aged from two years to over seventy, many of whom
were epileptic or dumb. That only 11 of 68 could 'tell time
to a minute', only four of 44 knew 'coins and weights and
could calculate fairly' and that only two of 43 could 'match
most compound shades' surely comes as no surprise, but
the good Doctor complained that:

> *[Educational] results are as good as can be expected from our miscellaneous collection of idiots so different and so inferior in type to those admitted to Earlswood or the Royal Albert Asylum for the seven Northern Counties.*

(But both were both private establishments, receiving idiots and imbeciles as children, and from middle class families, rather than the pauper population). However, he appears to have moderated his tone somewhat when he reviewed the outcome of the care 'Highfield' provided, after it had been operational for a few years:

> *Great results cannot be attained or expected here. 40 patients attend school, where their capacities are exercised from the simple appreciation of shapes and colours, to moderate attempts at reading, writing and plain figures. However, many of the adult idiots reward the care bestowed on them by a marked improvement in habits, and by a more systematic exercise of the capacities they possess. They continue to be usefully employed in a large proportion.*[6]

He had plainly revised his opinion of 1853:

> *Cases such as these are not likely to be materially benefitted by any special course of training applied to them...*[7]

ENDNOTES

1. He was later to become MS of the District Lunatic Asylum, Kilkenny, Co Kerry, Ireland.
2. Down's Syndrome: a syndrome of mental impairment and characteristic physical features, first described by Dr Langdon Down in 1866. Now known to be a genetic disorder of the chromosomes (trisomy 21).

3. Conolly *Construction of Lunatic Asylums* p159.
4. It was renamed Middlefield Hospital in 1948 and part of the NHS, eventually closing in the 1990s. Today it is part of Warwickshire College.
5. WHP *Annual Report 1862.*
6. WHP *Annual Report 1874.*
7. WHP *Annual Report 1869.*

CHAPTER 6

LATER YEARS

The asylum attempted to integrate itself into the community, at least to some degree:

> *As much personal liberty as is considered consistent with safety is accorded to the patients; a few have unrestricted freedom of the grounds; and those that are considered fit, and have the opportunity, are allowed to pass occasional days with friends; and almost all are encouraged to join in walks about the grounds or neighbourhood, accompanied by attendants; all of which forms an important constituent in their hygienic treatment, and must be regarded as a healthful, and consequently, in such a community, very useful occupation of time.*[1]

This must have been universal practice in English asylums at the time, for John Bucknill, 'when failing health had compelled him to seek a change of air and scene with as little fatigue as possible', made a tour of some thirteen American asylums in the Spring of 1875, and reported:

> *I nowhere saw any number of patients enjoying out-door exercise [...] the days of May were bright, sunny and delicious, and such days with us would have turned out the population of our asylums into the gardens and the grounds, overflowing into the country beyond.*[2]

But the alienists' initial hopes of enabling recovery from mental illness for many of their patients, following their admission to the asylum, where they would receive expert care – and cure – were increasingly disappointed with the passage of time, and this can be seen in the tone of Dr Parsey's reports as the asylum moved into the 1870s:

Of the 53 males admitted [in 1869], only 20 were labouring under forms of insanity presenting any reasonable prospect of recovery. It will be seen that, as regards this very important feature in the success of Asylum treatment, no very great scope has been given for the exercise of the appliances at our command.

And in 1870:

I have again to report my almost yearly remark on the singularly unfavourable nature of the male admissions as regards recovery. The higher wages and skilled occupations of Birmingham and its surrounding industrial district act as a continual inducement to emigration for the more active intelligences and more robust physically among the working classes of the county, leaving to the agricultural districts all the feeble constitutions and more inactive minds, which are the main feeders of the degenerate male population of the asylum. However, of the female admissions nearly two thirds have been cases affording prospect of recovery.

1875 saw the asylum's population rise to 537, with a disproportionate number of very elderly admissions. No longer was the asylum 'a place of refuge' for a manageable number of patients, in the early stages of their illness and all known personally to the Medical Superintendent, who had an adequate number of attendants to look after them.

1875 also saw an employee named Sarah Thornborough leave the asylum; she was aged seventy one, and had been a

Night Nurse for eighteen years. Dr Parsey reported to the Visitors that she was 'worn out by the nature of her duties': the Visitors awarded her a pension of £30 per annum, and she enjoyed six years of financially secure retirement.

One can sense the beginnings of chronic exhaustion in Dr Parsey too:

> *Admission of the very elderly entails on the asylum unfair responsibilities: for these patients of advanced years have to mix with others of different ages and influenced by insane impulses and have to be tended by persons whose chief qualifications are considered to be those of attendants on the insane rather than nurses of the infirm.*

But the Commissioners in Lunacy pronounced gaily:

> *During our passage through the wards many of the patients spoke very favourably of the kindness and attention shown to them by Dr Parsey, by whom the Asylum and its inmates continue to be superintended in a most creditable and efficient manner.*

Their indifference would prove to be the final straw.

★

In 1875, at its Annual General Meeting in Dublin, Henry Parsey was elected President of the 'Medico-Psychological Association' for 1876. Both his teachers had been President in AMOAHI days, and another distinguished alienist who had been an Assistant at the Hatton Asylum in his early career was to follow him in 1878: (Sir) James Crichton-Browne – Wardle Bowen's successor as AMO at Hatton for a short period and a future Medical Superintendent of Newcastle and Wakefield asylums – by then a Lord Chancellor's Visitor in Lunacy.

To be elected President was, of course, a great personal honour, bringing with it recognition from an International membership that Hatton was a centre of excellence, but there was a Presidential Address to give at the Royal College of Physicians in London, and, no doubt, also many administrative burdens to be shouldered during the year, in addition to his Asylum responsibilities.

Dr Parsey began his Presidential Address with an apology for contributing little towards 'a more extended knowledge of insanity and its treatment' apart from his clinical teaching of the junior doctors at the Hatton Asylum, and his inability to 'make an occasion like this the vehicle for new ideas, and new chains of reasoning'.

He then commented that whilst all the early Superintendents of asylums had banished restraint as a mode of treatment therein, they had not really made any attempt at mental recuperation and the restoration of social skills of their charges. Hanwell under Conolly had allowed dances, where the Assistant Matron playing the piano, but only female patients took part, until Hatton became the first asylum to allow:

> *the mingling of the sexes in social dances and other homely amusements, the liberty to walk about the country with their attendants, and other such apparent trifles, conducive as much to freedom of action, as to the personal and domestic comfort of those who constituted my new charge.*

The mingling of the sexes had been 'an innovation which then involved a very great deal of consideration'.[3] And a certain amount of alarm among his contemporaries. He then went on to discuss the problem of the large numbers of persons of diseased minds that have become a burden on the community', and 'the increasing tendency to shelter many of them within the walls of County Asylums, though their mental condition did not warrant so costly a form of management.'

He had three suggestions: adding wards to workhouses; building new facilities specifically for the demented or adopting Scotland's 'family treatment' model, perhaps close to present asylums, which could provide supervision.

However, after further debate, he considered none of the above was a suitable solution: in urban areas there would be overcrowding, lack of indoor or outdoor occupation, poor supervision and exposure of such patients to all the vicissitudes of the city and in the rural regions 'the tediousness of long journeys from districts often only partially opened up by railways' would result in infrequent visiting of the patients and fragmentation of families.

He regretted he was unable to come to any serious conclusion as to the best course of action, and felt he could do no more than leave the dilemma for the body of membership to consider.[4]

All of which is understandable: after all, had the problem a simple solution no doubt it would already have been implemented. In fact, there was no answer at all, and so the numbers of 'imbeciles and dements' within asylums continued to rise inexorably – to find themselves cared for in the 'back wards', with the 'dirty' (incontinent) patients and the chronically psychotic.

*

In 1841 the population of England and Wales was 15,906,741 with 75 percent of the population living and employed in the countryside. By 1881, numbers had risen to 25,974,439, with 75 percent of the population working in industry and services in the expanding towns.[138]

By the end of the 1870s, the asylum contained a total of more than 650 patients, and Henry Parsey was certainly feeling the strain of his duties as Superintendent to the extent that by May 1882 he was contemplating early retirement on health grounds, but the Visitors were very alarmed at this suggestion, and he was granted a Deputy Medical Superintendent in place of his second Assistant.

He approached Dr Herbert Sankey, then SMO at Prestwich County Asylum, Manchester, who had been his AMO back in 1876, who accepted the offer of the new position, and joined the asylum again on 5 September 1882.

He formally expressed his thanks to the Committee in his Annual Report of January 1883:

> *This kindly concession, on the part of your Committee, to what I am afraid I can only regard as a failing capacity for work in myself, enables me to continue to hold a position here from which I should have otherwise felt it incumbent on me to ask you to relieve me.*

But it was too little, too late: Henry Parsey would continue as Superintendent at the Asylum for less than a year.

ENDNOTES

1. *WHP Annual Report 1869.*
2. Bucknill *Notes on Asylums for the Insane in America.*
3. Obituary of Miss Matilda Giddings, Conolly's Assistant Matron at Hanwell Asylum, *BJPsych* July 1900 617-8.
4. *Journal of Mental Science* October 1876.
5. Census figures for England & Wales 1841 & 1881.

CHAPTER 7

WAS THERE LIFE OUTSIDE THE ASYLUM?

Was there any social life for Dr Parsey – and his family – outside the confines of the asylum and its onerous duties? His Terms of Service on his appointment to the asylum, as set out in the Lunacy Act of 1845, dictated he must 'never absent himself for one night or more without the previous written consent of one or more of the Committee of Visitors and then only on condition of his providing a person properly qualified to reside in the asylum, and perform his duties during his absence': this must have been extremely restrictive for him and his young family in the years before he was joined by an Assistant Medical Officer.

The diaries of 1882-84 tell us very briefly of his own (quite hectic) professional and social life, with glimpses of family activities in Julie's case – riding, playing the organ in chapel and first aid training – but nothing of Edward's recreational activities at all. Might he have been a cricketer and also played on the asylum's idiosyncratic cricket ground? Disappointingly he is not listed in any of Leamington College's First Xl cricket teams, but he appears to have taken part in asylum 'entertainments' and in some amateur dramatics. His was an artistic temperament, presumably.

Dr Parsey had been instrumental in arranging weekly

'entertainments' for the patients of the asylum during the winter months when outdoor activities were curtailed, and there are newspaper reports of a few of these.

On 1 March 1873 the Leamington Spa Courier reported a concert given to the attendants and some eighty patients of the asylum by 'ladies and gentlemen residing in Warwick and the neighbourhood, and friends of Dr Parsey, to show appreciation of the attendants' endeavours in providing winter amusements for the patients'.

Among the musical items performed were duets by Dr Procter (flute) and Julie Parsey.[1] The Courier correspondent wrote 'Dr Procter is a very clever amateur flautist, and his performance coupled with that of Miss Parsey, who, though young [she would be 20 the following May] is a pianist of no mean order, drew forth loud and hearty applause from his hearers'. Julie also sang a solo 'Will he come?' by Sullivan, described as 'the gem of the evening'.[2]

On 21 April 1877 the Courier reported a morning concert and an evening entertainment which had been given in the recreation hall of the Asylum 'in aid of a Fund for Assistance of Discharged Patients', during the previous week.

A number of notable local persons were among the audience for the morning concert, including Sir RNC Hamilton, Bart., and party; Mrs Dugdale from Wroxall Abbey; the Rev Dr & Mrs Dickins (the Asylum's Chaplain) and, of course, Dr & Mrs Parsey. The concert began with a piano solo and was followed by a glee, sung by a choir of the asylum's attendants, accompanied by Julie Parsey at the piano. 'Miss Parsey had bestowed great pains in practicing them, and the result was exceeding gratifying' reported the Courier's correspondent.

Julie went on to sing 'The Sailor Boy's Farewell' and accompany Mr Sharpe (an attendant) in a selection for 'clarionette' and piano, and a number of other songs were performed 'creditably', but lest it is thought that the correspondent was lacking in critical musical faculties, he also reported that 'the Rev HC Courtney gave but a poor account of the air "Fair is my Love" from Bennett's "May Queen", the music not being within the compass of his voice'.[3]

The evening performance was equally well attended and the first half contained a number of musical items from the morning and others, performed by the choir, Mr Sharpe and Julie, and a one act comedietta 'A Cup of Tea', performed by four members of staff, concluded the evening.[4]

On 4 May 1878 the Courier reported that a large attendance of the public had turned out for an entertainment, this time 'in aid of the fund for patients' amusements.' The evening was divided into two parts: the first half was of vocal and instrumental music by the choir and a number of individual performers, which included a song for alto voice – 'The hay is in the mow' – sung by Julie Parsey and a 'clarionette' solo, again by Mr Sharpe, with Julie at the piano.

The second half was a farce, 'Pipkin's Rustic Retreat',[5] performed by asylum staff, including among others, Dr Wade and Dr Lilley, the two assistant medical officers. It appears to have been received well, the Leamington Courier reporting that it was 'ludicrously funny'.

On 25 January 1879 there was a 'fairly numerous attendance for an entertainment by officers of the establishment' , which comprised a 'petite comedy in one act' "Anything for a Change", by Shirley Brooks,[6] and featured Julie and also Edward in the cast list. This was Edward's debut, aged 13, in these 'entertainments': his third and last recorded appearance would be after he had left Cambridge.

★

There are also a number reports in the Courier of parochial meetings, more popularly known as 'penny readings', where Dr Parsey would occasionally be 'in the chair' directing proceedings and offering votes of thanks, and sometimes also giving readings or talks, usually of an educational nature. These were, for the most part, evening entertainments, held weekly during the winter months at various venues around the County. Those most frequently reported were held in the Court House in Warwick and drew an astonishingly loyal audience of townspeople. Other 'penny readings' were held weekly in the schoolroom adjacent to All Saints Church, Emscote and occasionally more widely afield at the Nelson Club, Warwick, in schoolrooms at Hampton-on-the-Hill and Hockley Heath and also in the Kenilworth Institute.

★

More formal social events often involved members of the family. Dr Parsey (of course) attended the opening of the asylum's new chapel on 14 November 1863; the inaugural meeting on 16 January 1869 (together with Dr Charles Bucknill) to consider the building of a new Idiot Asylum at Knowle; a number of meetings of the Warwick Natural History & Archaeological Society (of which he later became a Committee member); a meeting regarding a proposed chapel for the Warwick Union, at a cost of £700, to be paid for by private subscription (towards which he donated one guinea (£1.1s. 0d. or £1.05p), and the annual Mayoral Banquet in the Court House in Warwick for a number of years.

Julie was a soloist in a concert in the County Hall, Warwick, in aid of the Idiot Asylum at Knowle on 12

October 1878; at a concert of the Warwick Amateur Music Society on 19 October 1878 in the Leamington Institute; she also sang at 'entertainments' at Hampton-on-the-Hill on 25 October and 2 November 1882 ('proceeds towards an harmonium for the school'), and after her father had died she was to attend an entertainment at the Nelson Club, in aid of the Primrose League.[7]

And even Edward continued his amateur dramatics too after his father died: he was to appear on 8 January 1887 in Emscote Mill's Dining Hall in a production of 'A Scrap of Paper' by Palgrave Simpson, performed by ' a company of well-known local amateurs', in a period of his life, after leaving Cambridge, and before he completed his medical studies, when very little indeed is known of his activities.[8]

★

But life outside the asylum was not entirely giddy social events: in spite of his Terms of Service stating that 'he shall not engage in any professional or other business or employment except that of the asylum', Dr Parsey also made medical consultations outside the Asylum (recorded in his diaries) and undertook frequent public professional appearances of a medico-legal nature, when he was called as expert witness to give an opinion as to a defendant's sanity in trials held in the County Court in Warwick.

Two occasions when he was called to give evidence are worth studying in detail. The first involved a married woman by the name of Selina Cranmore, aged 32, from Berkswell, who was accused of the murder of Thomas Cranmore, her infant son.

Selina Cranmore had been admitted to Hatton on 16 April 1858 from the County gaol whence she had been committed for trial on a charge of murder, on a warrant signed by S H Walpole, the Home Secretary, under an Act of Parliament 'for the confinement and maintenance of insane prisoners'. (He appears to make a habit of committing persons to the Hatton asylum).

At the trial in July, Counsel for the prosecution stated that, from the woman's own statement, there was no doubt that she was guilty of the crime with which she was charged. The question was whether she was in a sane state of mind at the time. Mr Harry Adkins a surgeon apothecary with a practice in Meriden, gave evidence that he had attended her twice in three days following her confinement – it was not usual practice for general practitioners to attend women in childbirth at this time – and did not think she was in her right senses. She had apprehensions of becoming poor, which he believed to be a delusion. He had thought it necessary to caution the attendant. Although a man in the village had hanged himself at about this time, Mr Adkins did not think that event was responsible for her mental state.[9]

On the twenty-fourth day following her confinement, he was called to the house where he found Mrs Cranmore at her cottage, sitting in her chair, crying, with the dead child in its cradle. He examined the infant's body and was satisfied that the cause of death was strangulation. He asked her how this had happened. Mrs Cranmore said the child had been crying; it had become burdensome to her and she had strangled it with a piece of strong tape.

Dr Parsey was called to give his expert opinion: he said he had been requested by the Coroner to examine Mrs Cranmore eight days after the event. She was unquestionably of unsound mind when he saw her and had since been constantly deluded.

The asylum's casebook for 1858 contains, in his own handwriting, Dr Parsey's history and examination on admission of every patient, with subsequent clinical notes made during their period of admission, however protracted.

Regarding Selina Cranmore he wrote:

Admitted 16 April. Wife of bricklayer. Last autumn had a long illness; this appears to have caused her much anxiety. She was also in the family way. She became despairing and began to fancy their affairs were in so embarrassed a state that they would all come to ruin and that nothing could save them. Her manner altered and she became as if she was always pondering or thinking and said her soul was lost and wished she was dead, that the meal she was taking would be her last and that the children would starve. All these statements were drawn with some difficulty from her.

Was confined latter end of February about half an hour after her next door neighbour had hung himself.

No medical man had attended her at her confinement but one was sent for four days afterwards. He left her with the impression she was in a morbid state of mind and advised her sister who was visiting to watch her closely.

On 31 March her husband came home at about 9pm. His wife came to the door and said she had been all over the parish looking for him to tell him that the child (their fourth) was dead.

On examination she had much guarded depression not arising so much from the destruction of her child as but from a morbid impression that they must all come to ruin, for her husband's affairs were so involved that they cannot be put straight.

Says she destroyed the child because she thought it such a burden to her and she could better do her duty if it were gone. The idea that she could do wrong did not at the time enter her head. Never had similar feelings with her other children.

12 July. Felt much more acutely her present position and was much depressed by the idea that nothing could save her from being hanged and that there was no hope of forgiveness for her in this world or the

142

*next. General state of mind much as at prior interview; spoke very
feelingly about her dead child but said it all appeared a dream to her.
Also though listening attentively to all that is said to her about her own
condition and the lenient view taken in her case in sending her here
and appearing to understand and take consolation from it, she at the
end of the consultation expressed extreme grief and distress and feels
assured that everybody is against her and that they intend to hang her
soon. Expression that of fixed moderate anxious melancholy.*

At the trial he stated he thought that a man's hanging himself
would have a bad effect upon the mind of a woman in
confinement. Her mental state was slowly improving; she had
that morning come to Court from the Lunatic Asylum, and
she now fully understood the position in which she now stood.

The jury acquitted her of murder of her son, Thomas
Cranmore, on the grounds of insanity.

The Judge requested that Mrs Cranmore should
continue to remain in the asylum and Dr Parsey concurred,
observing that the woman's recovery had been somewhat
retarded by the anxiety connected with the trial.[10]

The condition of 'puerperal psychosis' merits
consideration for a moment: it is an uncommon but an
extremely alarming sequel to childbirth, for the mother
and the family and is a heavy responsibility for those
physicians who are entrusted with ensuring proper care
and supervision of mother and child, for recovery can take
a number of months, and there remains a high likelihood of
recurrence in future confinements.

Dr Parsey's clinical records and the general tenor of the
newspaper report of the trial proceedings suggest the Court
had a certain sympathy towards Mrs Cranmore, and was
seeking grounds for her acquittal of murder.

It had long been recognised that childbirth could disturb
a mother's mental equanimity, sometimes so much so that

she would kill her child, so the Courts looked for mitigating circumstances, and usually found them in the medical men's opinion that at the time of the event the mother was 'of unsound mind'.

Yet it wasn't until 1922 that legislation was introduced, reducing the crime of infanticide to manslaughter, whilst a newly-delivered (legally, this period of time was within twelve months of delivery) woman's balance of mind was disturbed.

And so Mrs Cranmore was returned from the courtroom to Hatton asylum. Dr Parsey had suggested to the Court that her mental state was recovering, and her casebook entries do indeed confirm a slow recovery:

16 September. Trial end of July. Has once or twice evinced a little confusion of thought. On the whole has been going on satisfactorily and may be considered convalescent.

30 April 1859. Has been satisfactory both mentally and bodily since last report and by an order from the Sec. of State was discharged.

Courtesy of S H Walpole, Home Secretary, Selina Cranmore returned to her husband and family in Berkswell, and they took up family life once more. But fate was to deal them a further bitter blow: on 31 January 1861, Selina died, with her husband in attendance, aged 34, from 'consumption present two years'.[11]

Had she contracted tuberculosis whilst she was being held in the asylum? It appears likely. The 1858 casebook entries for two other female patients admitted to the asylum at about the same time as Selina are of some importance in this matter. Firstly:

5 March 1858. E. S. 34. Single. Prostitute. Has for some months known to be extremely strange and eccentric and at times excited but having committed no breach of the peace and continuing to gain her livelihood in her usual way she was not interfered with until yesterday when she made a disturbance and insulted people in the streets of Leamington. She was removed to the station. Was there very excitable talking incoherently saying people had entered her house and she was being constantly watched and that people had put arsenic in her food.

12 April. Still much incoherence and restlessness but no active excitement.

31 May. Confirmed phthisis [a medical term for pulmonary tuberculosis which is highly infectious] set in from effects of which she died on the present date. For many days previous to her death her mental capacities seem to have entirely changed, becoming quite reasonable and calm and could talk coherently.

At least the asylum continued her care in her terminal illness, despite the apparent recovery of her mental state.

Secondly:

2 August 1858. S.W. 24. Married. Factory woman. Married about four years. About four years ago was considered to be insane but not removed from home. From that time her manner has been strange and she appeared not to know what she was about. Has been subject to fits in which she struggles, foams at the mouth, sometimes bites her tongue and falls out of bed. In the past week or more she has become incoherent often rambling and violent. Has taken little food for several days. Is stated to be in 4th or 5th month of gestation.

16 April 1859. Since last report has constantly been afflicted with epileptic fits mainly attacking her at night. Her bodily health has greatly given way and for several months has been confined to bed with phthisis pulmonalis and on the present date she died. During her

confinement in the asylum she was delivered of a male child and it was
after this that her health began to fail; at the birth she had a violent
attack of haemorrhage which greatly weakened her.

So, it appears there were (at least) two cases of highly infectious tuberculosis in the women's wing of the asylum, concurrently with Selina Cranmore's admission. Probably not unusual, for the first documentation of a patient undergoing treatment for 'phthisis' (tuberculosis of the lung) was in the Journal of patients undergoing medical treatment in the asylum, and is dated 26 November 1853.

★

Dr Parsey had suggested in his Presidential Address that 'family care' might be an option for more imbeciles and dements, provided the asylum had the powers to readmit them to the asylum if there was a deterioration in their mental state which resulted in uncontrollable behaviour. He gave an instance of 'homicide under insane impulse by a simpleton' who had lived for many years with his family, but who became deluded and killed an elderly woman with a pitchfork.

These are the details of the case: John Tennant, a farm labourer aged 80, and his wife, Ann, aged 79, lived in Long Compton. Their neighbours of many years were a couple called Haywood, and their 45 year-old son James, who was described as 'a half-witted farm labourer' whose conduct was considered in the village to be 'strange at times' and who 'harboured ideas about evil spirits and witches'. The Haywood family considered the Tennants to be witches, and were exerting a malign influence over James.

Returning home one evening he attacked Ann Tennant with a pitchfork he had been using earlier at work in a field of beans, stabbing her in the head and legs. She died later that evening.

James had gone to work with a gallon of ale (it was standard practice for harvest workers to be given beer but not for them to drink such an amount too quickly, said a witness) and at his arrest he claimed that witches had stopped him from working for three hours. The arresting Police Constable's opinion was that this was probably due to drunkenness. The Warwick County Gaol surgeon, Mr J R Nunn[12], stated that James had a strong belief in witches and believed he was possessed.

Dr Parsey's opinion was sought. He stated he had examined James Hayward on two occasions after his arrest and found him to be:

> *a man of general feeble character, badly developed head, which in conjunction with congenital deafness and impediment of speech marked him as a man of very weak intellect [which suggests he had a degree of physical brain damage, such as cerebral palsy]. He was labouring under a strong delusion on the subject of witchcraft [...] and was not responsible for what he did in connection with that subject. Although he was aware he was in trouble he failed to realise the gravity of his offence.*[13]

Dr Parsey thought belief in witches was common in Warwickshire; there were patients in the asylum who thought they were bewitched, and whose relatives preferred to consider them to be bewitched than insane.

The evidence seems to point fairly conclusively to a verdict of insanity – but a doctor's opinion does not confirm mental illness is present – and the judge in his summing up was dismissive of the medical evidence:

> *A poor helpless old creature [...] had been killed by the accused, whilst labouring under the influence of a superstition and ignorance*

discreditable to a set of savages, let alone to a civilized country like England.

He doubted very much whether there was in this case much of the impulse spoken of by the medical gentlemen, and more of a case of intention and therefore directed the jury to find the accused guilty of murder.

However, the jury took only a few minutes to acquit Haywood as insane, and reluctantly, the judge sentenced Haywood to be detained in the asylum at Hatton at Her Majesty's Pleasure.[14]

Following sentencing, he was then overheard to say:

'I cannot help it. I laid down the law correctly.' [15]

Dr Parsey's opinion that belief in witches in Warwickshire is common appears to be correct: as recently as 1945 Charles Walton, a farm worker aged 74, was found dead on Meon Hill, an Iron Age fort near Lower Quinton, just a few miles from Stratford-upon-Avon; he had been killed with the bill hook he had been using to lay a hedge, but had also had a pitchfork driven through his body into the ground beneath, suggesting a superstitious element to the attack. The crime has never been solved.

Perhaps James Haywood was fortunate to receive the sanctuary of the asylum.

ENDNOTES

1. The flautist was presumably Rev Lovell Procter MA, Julie's maternal uncle, but he had no doctorate degree, according to Crockford's Clerical Directory of that year.
2. Song by Sir Arthur Sullivan (1842-1900). English composer.

Collaborated with WS Gilbert in the 'Savoy Operas'.

3. *'May Queen'* composed by Sir William Sterndale Bennett (1816-1875); English composer and friend of Robert Schumann.

4. Originally *'Une Tasse de Thé'* (1869) by Charles Nuitter, (who also translated the libretto of Wagner's *'Lohengrin'* into French).

5. By Thomas John Williams, written in 1866.

6. Charles William Shirley Brooks (1816-1874). Novelist and editor of *'Punch'* magazine. The obituary which forms the inscription on the Ashes urn at Lord's is attributed to him.

7. The Primrose League was an organization 'for supporting the Conservative cause.' Founded in 1883 it was finally wound up in 2004.

8. *'A Scrap of Paper'* (1861). Best known play of John Palgrave Simpson (1807-1887); a Victorian playwright of melodramas.

9. Referred to in the press as 'Mr' Harry Adkins, although he had held the 'College and Hall' double qualification of MRCS, LSA., since 1842.

10. *Royal Leamington Spa Courier* 7 August 1858.

11. DC Selina Cranmore GRO: 1861 March Meriden Vol 6b p213.

12. John Robert Nunn; Jury Street, Warwick q 1862 MRCS, LSA.

13. *Royal Leamington Spa Courier* 18 December 1875.

14. 139 Lethbridge *Foul Deeds* p114-123.

15. *Royal Leamington Spa Courier* 18 December 1875.

CHAPTER 8

'THE TRIVIAL ROUND, THE COMMON TASK':
HENRY PARSEY'S PERSONAL DIARIES 1882– 1884,
WITH AN AFTERWORD

This chapter contains a personal account of the final two years of Dr Parsey's life, starting on 1 January 1882 and ending with his death on 10 January 1884, together with an Afterword, and is transcribed verbatim from his small personal diary (with some editing).

Explanatory footnotes are also provided regarding people, places and events described therein. His diary has very idiosyncratic punctuation: this has been standardized, as far as possible, to allow for ease of reading. His occasionally impenetrable illegibility has been indicated in the text of the diary where this occurs.

1882

January

1 Sunday. Confined to house by inflamed eye. Temperature very mild for the season.

2   Mrs Ellerton & son in the afternoon.[1]

---

1   Charlotte Ellerton, wife of Dr Frederick Ellerton MRCS,

3   Temperature in my dressing room at 7.30am 52° F. A heavy gale with rain last night. Splendid mild sunshiny day today. Wind W.

6   Haseley Hall.[2] Continuous mild weather, unsettled, gusty, much rain, alternating with bright clear skies. Temperature at 10am taken out of doors, in the shade 57° F. Edward[3] taking first riding lessons in the grounds yesterday and today.

10 Bought sidesaddle for Julie.

11 Julie and Ted both trotting: with promise of very good seat.

Lucy Blenkinsop[4] here yesterday & today coaching for ambulance exam with Julie. Weather like delightful spring though still much rain.

12 Visited Mrs Claridge[5] with Dr Bullock.[6]

LSA, in practice at Lindley House, 69 Arlington Avenue, Leamington. Son John Frederick Ellerton (b 1853), at the time a 'student of medicine', who would go on to qualify MRCS, LRCP and enter practice at 9 Priory Terrace, Leamington. Reason for consultation with WHP is not known.

2   Haseley Hall; a late 18c. mansion. Sold to Sir James Sawyer MD JP, Consulting Physician, Queen's Hospital, Birmingham, in 1889. Now luxury apartments. Reason for visit by WHP is not known.

3   Edward William Henry Parsey (b 1864), WHP's son; Julie is Julia Mary Parsey (b 1853), WHP's daughter.

4   Lucy Eliza Blenkinsop (b 1864), family friend & stepdaughter of Richard Child Heath of Heath & Blenkinsop, Solicitors, 50 New Street, Warwick.

5   Probably Jane Claridge (b 1810), a widow living in Dame Alice Leigh's Almshouses, Stoneleigh and 'partially blind', according to 1881 census.

6   Thomas William Bullock MRCS, LSA, in practice at 37 Jury Street, Warwick.

17 Mrs Nelson's Ball.[7] Need spectacles.[8]

18 Mrs Claridge with Dr Bullock. Dense fog; barometer fair last few days. Has reached 30.9 inches.

20 1½ degrees of frost registered by sheltered barometer. Sent carriage for repair yesterday.[9]

22 Julie laid up yesterday with bad throat.

23 Birthday of my dear wife.

25 Last few days extremely mild & fine. Slight hoar frost early this morning. Sheltered thermometer registered 30°. Quarterly & annual committee. Mrs Smith (Back)[10] and Mrs Claridge. Let meadows of Asylum – Rent £24 a year from 25th last December tenants to pay all rates etc.

26 Ted & Duge's[11] theatricals.[12] Slight early morning frost.

---

7   Ellen Augusta Nelson (b 1834), wife of George Henry Nelson (b 1838), of 'The Lawn', Emscote. Owner of George Nelson, Dale & Co., Gelatine Manufacturers, Emscote Mill, Warwick, which employed 119 men, 37 boys, 14 women and 22 girls at the time. 'The Lawn' became a preparatory school until its sale in 1999 for redevelopment as a housing estate.

8   In the only portrait photograph of WHP available, he is wearing spectacles. Presumably this dates the photograph to 1882 at the earliest.

9   WHP had a carriage and attendant, provided by the asylum. A general practitioner would have travelled either on foot or, more commonly, on horseback, or possibly in a two-wheeled self-driven gig. The Clergy however, were very much reduced, for the most part, to visiting their parishioners on foot. This became a bone of contention in 1885 for the R.C. Chaplain, because 'the visits entail a certain amount of hardship upon me for I have no other means of getting to the Asylum but by walking the distance [2 miles] which takes me a full hour to do it in'. He resigned, after seven years in post.

10 Unidentified.

11 'Duge' (pronounced 'Doo-gee') was an affectionate family name for Julie.

12 A reasonably frequent event in the asylum, and very

29 Yesterday and today very heavy rain. Today somewhat colder.
30 Change of wind to N.E. has for many weeks with slight intervals of WNW been between W & S. Heavy snow has fallen.
31 Julie went to the ambulance examination in Leamington.

February

1 Edward returned to Leamington College.[13]
   Mrs Claridge with Dr Bullock. 1° frost registered in the morning.
2 Julie confined to bed with great malaise, cold & rheumatism.
4 Julie better; slight frost early this morning.
5 Thirtieth anniversary of our marriage.[14] Duge [Julie] confined to bed.
6 Julie better today – Julia and myself dined with the Heaths of Myton Grange.[15] On return found Julie

---

popular, at which WHP's children would assist in providing entertainment for the patients, their families, friends and staff. A number of patients played musical instruments and attendants were often recruited if they also had the ability.
13 Leamington College, (Binswood Hall), founded in 1847 'for the purpose of providing a classical, mathematical, and general training of the highest order, on moderate terms, combined with religious instruction in accordance with the principles of the Church of England'. The building is very elegant, of red and grey bricks in the Tudor style. Recently converted into luxury apartments.
14 WHP married Julia Procter on 5 February 1852, at All Saints Church, Bishop Burton, Nr Beverley, Yorkshire. Julia's father, Rev William Procter was the officiating minister.
15 Richard Child Heath, Solicitor. Also Clerk to the Committee of Visitors of the asylum and Under Sheriff of Warwickshire. He, his wife Margaret and their children were family friends

in state of high pyrexia; came on about 9pm. Cough distressing congestion of upper part of left lung.

7 Julie on the whole better. Much less pyrexia at night.

8 Julie not so well. Cough much more troublesome and increased pyrexia.

9 Julie fell into sound sleep about 4am. Slept till 9.45 looks much refreshed. Cough greatly reduced, temperature normal (98.5°). Passed a good day: at 9pm temp 99.4°. Dr Thursfield saw her with me.[16]

13 Julie continues satisfactory progress. Bronchial secretions diminished. Cough free. Continues remarkably mild weather.

15 At Warwick Assizes. Trial of attendant at Birmingham Borough Lunatic Asylum for manslaughter of a patient.[17] Acquitted. Very feeble case. Judge shortened trial by summing up without prosecuting counsel's reply.

16 Julie going on well. Julia quite knocked up yesterday & today.

17 Mrs Nuttings.[18]

18 Wagonette[19] sent home from coachbuilders after

---

of WHP. Myton Grange was a fine Victorian residence, built in 1857. In the 1930s it became a children's home, later to be demolished. Myton Hospice and the present housing development now occupy the site.

16 Dr Thomas Thursfield MD (Aberdeen), MRCS, LRCP, in practice at 16 York Terrace, Leamington. Family doctor to WHP. Understandable concern for Julie shown by WHP: in the pre-antibiotic era pneumonia had a 30% mortality.

17 It is not known whether WHP attended Court to give an opinion or merely as an interested observer. See Appendix 9 for a newspaper report of the court proceedings.

18 Unidentified.

19 Probably the same carriage as the one in the photograph of Mrs Parsey outside the asylum. This is more correctly termed a 'fiacre', named after the Hotel St Fiacre in Paris, where it was used from the 1640s to drive patrons to the hospice at

thorough dress up. Sent half yearly accounts to Louise Procter[20] and Susan Oldham.[21] Julia still very unwell.

20 Visited Winson Green Asylum.[22] Yesterday Dr Thursfield came over in afternoon and made a thorough & satisfactory examn. of Julie's chest.

21 Called at the College Leamington to see Edward who has been unwell last few days.[23] Found him getting better. Also called on Mr Owen (Vice Principal) about Edward's arrangements for Cambridge.

26 Julie resumed organ in chapel.[24] Julia still very unwell.

28 Thirtieth anniversary of my entering into residence here.[25]

March

1 Went to Leamington with Julie to receive her St John's ambulance certificate.[26] Julia still much debility. Great rainfall during last few days. Season continues extremely mild. Much general sickness.

Saint-Fiacre. A very stylish mode of transport at the time.

20 Louisa May Procter (b 1824), sister of WHP's wife Julia.

21 Unidentified.

22 All Saints Mental Asylum was built in 1850 to accommodate 300 lunatics on land adjacent to Winson Green Prison, which had opened the previous year. Its first MS and contemporary of WHP was Dr Thomas Green MRCS, LSA. It closed in 2001 and is now part of the prison.

23 Presumably Edward was boarding at the College.

24 Presumably Julie played the organ for asylum chapel services. In 1899, the then Clerk of the asylum was being paid an honorarium of £20 pa 'as organist'.

25 WHP had been appointed MS on 28 February 1852, but the asylum did not open to receive patients until 30 June that year.

26 Dr Thursfield organized and was an examiner for the St John's Ambulance Association First Aid Certificate course (for ladies) held in the Public Hall in Leamington: it attracted some 200 entrants each year.

8 Julia continues an invalid although slowly improving. Troubled for last few days with pain & swelling in left leg if not carefully rested. Went out for a ride today in covered carriage. Weather continues very mild.

11 Entered Edward (through Mr Owen) at St Peter's College, Cambridge for 2nd October (caution money paid £15).

17 To London. My sister Mrs Baker.[27]

18 At Savoy Theatre "Patience".[28]

19 At Bayswater (sister Louisa).[29]

20 Mr Sawhill [?] on M A Procter's[30] business. Sent her cheque for £40. Called at Bethlem (Haydons).[31]

21 S Ken Museum.[32] Corks in the evening.

22 Louisa spent the day with us.

23 Home.

25 Went to see new house with builder Mr Mason

---

27 Elder sister Elizabeth (b 1819), now widowed and living in Islington.

28 A comic opera; music by Arthur Sullivan & lyrics by WS Gilbert. It ran for 578 performances at the Savoy Theatre.

29 Louisa (b 1830), a spinster; one of WHP's four younger sisters.

30 Unidentified (presumed a member of WHP's wife's family).

31 George Haydon (b 1824), barrister-at-law, who was living with his wife Clarissa and their four children in Bethlem Hospital in Southwark (now the Imperial War Museum), where he had been Clerk of Bethlem & Bridewell Hospitals since 1853. WHP and he had been colleagues at the Devon County Asylum before their subsequent appointments. He had also been one of Bucknill's volunteers during his time in Devon.

32 The Natural History Museum, South Kensington, which had opened the previous year (1881). WHP took a great interest in the natural world, especially meteorology, and was known to have studied the writings of Charles Darwin. Corks remain unidentified.

(Leamington).[33]

30 Leamington. Called at Mrs White's, Grosvenor Villa.[34]

31 Lunch with Mrs Pele.[35] Duge at ambulance lecture.

April

1 Edward & Millington[36] over from the Leamington College for the afternoon and evening. Called at Claridges with Dr Bullock.

3 My sixty-first birthday. In good health for my age though somewhat damaged from sleeplessness and probably nervous overstrain during the last few years. Have reason for much thankfulness that all my domestic & social relations are happy and my position comfortable and sufficiently prosperous.[37]

With Dr Lawson Heale[38] to Warwick G.W.R. Stationmaster.

---

33 Approaching the age of 61, WHP may have been either contemplating retirement and removal from the tied accommodation provided at the asylum, or possibly speculating in property (see entries in the diary re. a Drury Lane property).

34 Mrs Amelia White, widow, living at Grosvenor Villa, St Mary's Road, Leamington, with her daughter Gertrude (18), a butler, a housekeeper and two domestic servants; 'income by shares' according to 1881 census. Reason for WHP's visit is not known.

35 Unidentified.

36 Presumably a school friend from the College, but otherwise unidentified.

37 WHP's income in 1882 was £800 pa, together with a furnished house, coal, gas, vegetables and 'feed for one horse'. (A contemporary general practitioner, established in practice for ten years, would earn about £600 pa).

38 Dr Alfred Lawson Heale MRCS, LSA, in practice at Holly Lodge, Coten End, Warwick. Outcome of visit to stationmaster not known.

4/5 Called at Dickins'.[39]

Mr Bourne from Broom called.[40]

Horse agility Leamington. Duge at ambulance lecture. Mrs Dickins.

8 Went over to Rev J G Bourne Broom Rectory near Stourbridge. Wrote to Mrs Lands Coe[41] about house in Leamington.

10 Called at the Matron's.[42]

11 Mrs Lands Coe called in the morning. Claridges[43] in the afternoon. Saw with Dr Tibbutts[44] a poor Hatton woman. Wrote to Mr Bourne.

12 Called at Mrs Mullings.[45]

13 Dr Haynes[46] called about Miss Bourne.

---

39 Rev Thomas Bourne Dickins, Vicar of Emscote, and Chaplain to the asylum from 1860 until 1888 (whereupon he was succeeded by his son, Rev Richard Henry Dickins). Also a family friend, whose duties came to include conducting WHP's burial service, the marriage service of their son, Edward, in St Mary's, Warwick, in 1895, and the burial service of his widow, Julia, in 1896.

40 WHP also visited Rev Joseph Green Bourne, Rector of Broome, Nr Stourbridge, since 1859, regarding his sister, Sarah Bennitt Bourne. WHP only attended on the one occasion, but a considerable correspondence ensued.

41 Unidentified.

42 Elizabeth Kirkby (b 1846), a spinster, was Matron at the time.

43 WHP's visits were probably complementary to her general practitioner, Dr Bullock.

44 Dr John Tibbitts MD (St Andrew's), MRCS, LSA, in practice at 21 Jury Street, Warwick, where he lived with his wife, eight children, four domestic servants, including an 18-year old 'page', and a 'medical assistant', aged 41, according to the 1881 census. Hatton patient unidentified.

45 Unidentified.

46 Dr Frederick Harry Haynes MD (London), MRCS, in practice at 23 Parade, Leamington, also attending physician to the Warneford Hospital.

14 Leamington College sports. Julie ambulance lecture Windsor House 15 Parade.

15 Wrote Mrs Lands Coe declining house.[47] Called at Wroxall:[48] Mr C & Dr Thursfield there.

16.17.18. Correspondence with Rev J Minton about his sister-in-law Miss S Bourne.[49]

20 Dr & Mrs Ellerton spent afternoon with us. Mrs Barton[50] called.

21 Edward last few days inflamed uvula and chest.

24 Mrs Emily Stewart[51] came to help preparing for theatricals.

25 Second letter from Mr G Nelson and call from Dr Tebbitts concerning being present at operation on Mrs Nelson. Received letter from Mrs Linton telling me of the death of her sister Miss Bourne.[52]

---

47 Presumably WHP had second thoughts (for whatever reason) about proceeding with the purchase of the house.

48 Wroxall Abbey; built in the Victorian gothic style in 1866 by James Dugdale, High Sheriff of Warwickshire, on the site of an ancient Benedictine Priory. A girls school from 1936-1995 and now a luxury hotel. Reason for visit by WHP & Dr Thursfield is not known.

49 Why WHP should have spent three days on correspondence regarding 'Miss Bourne' is difficult to determine. However, Sarah Bennitt Bourne, spinster, was admitted to Ashwood House, a private asylum in Kingswinford, Worcs., ('where the climate is genial and the locality notoriously healthy'), on 17 April 1882. WHP may have been instrumental in arranging her admission to that asylum, with regard to the completion of the necessary committal papers, when personal attendance for examination of the patient was essential.

50 Unidentified.

51 Unidentified

52 Sarah Bennitt Bourne died on 23 April 1882, aged 47. Cause of death was 'Insanity; cardiac failure'. The certificate was signed by Dr George F Boddington MRCP, FRCS, 'occupier'

26 Visit from Commissioners in Lunacy. Dr Williams[53] also here 10.45 to 4.45pm.

Mrs Mason[54] in the evening helping to prepare for theatricals.

Dr Alfred Miller[55] new A.M.O. came unexpectedly in evening.

27 Commissioners in Lunacy in the morning. Asylum Committee midday. Operation on Mrs Louisa Nelson The Lawn Warwick by Mr Spencer Wells[56] at 4.30 – 5.15pm. Dr Tibbitts, Dr Haynes & myself present.[57]

(and proprietor) of Ashwood House.

53 Possibly Dr Samuel Williams MD, MRCS, LRCP, LSA, the MS of Sussex County Lunatic Asylum, Hayward's Heath.

54 Probably the Mrs Mason of 'Major & Mrs Mason' who stayed for supper on 27 April, but otherwise unidentified.

55 Dr Alfred Miller MB (TCD), later to become MS of the asylum in 1889.

56 Sir Thomas Spencer Wells (1818-1897|), FRCS, received his surgical training at Trinity College, Dublin, and St Thomas's Hospital. He was Surgeon to Queen Victoria from 1863-1896, and was created baronet in 1883. It was common practice for the moneyed Victorian middle classes to request physicians and surgeons to attend on them in their homes, hospital acquired infection being an ever-present concern. Medical men were able to travel extensively with the arrival of the railways, and surgeons would bring their surgical instruments, an anaesthetist colleague, and other accoutrements with them on domiciliary visits. No doubt George Nelson would have requested the best London surgeon he could obtain to attend his wife.

57 Surgical procedure undergone by Mrs Nelson is not known. She died on 19 November 1887, cause of death being 'Dyspepsia & constipation many months; Peritonitis with perforation of intestine a few hours'. The certificate was signed by Dr Tibbits. This last illness of an acute bowel perforation, peritonitis and rapid demise, (a complication of diverticular disease of the colon), continues to be a common

Theatricals in the Recreation Hall from 8 to 10.30pm 'One of you must marry'[58] and Cinderella. Went off admirably. Julie Cinderella Ted 'Prince Charming', about 350 present.

Major & Mrs Mason stayed to supper.

28 Called at Nelsons & Mrs Dickins. Julie at ambulance lecture. Very wet forenoon & hail in afternoon. At 8pm repetition of theatricals for patients.

29 Called at Nelsons & Mrs Dickins. Mrs Nelson going on very favourably. Temperature normal pulse nearly so. Mrs Burman[59] & Miss Sherrard left in very heavy rain downpour.

May

1 My old friend Archdeacon Woods[60] from British Columbia spent the morning with us. In afternoon called on Nelson and Dickins. Mrs N rather suffering from flatulence.

4 Mrs N quite satisfactory. Mrs D better.

---

cause of death. It was almost certainly unrelated to the operation performed by Mr Spencer Wells, (as he then was), on 27 April 1882. She was buried in Warwick Cemetery, her funeral being conducted by Rev Thomas Bourne Dickins, their parish priest. He would also conduct the funeral of her husband, George Henry Nelson, in 1898. The 'Spencer Wells forceps' is a surgical instrument designed by the great man and still used by surgeons today.

58 Title unidentified.

59 Possibly Sarah Burman, wife of Samuel Burman, saw miller, of Knowle Wood, who just possibly may have supplied coffins to the asylum. Miss Sherrard is unidentified.

60 Venerable Archdeacon Thomas Charles Woods, BA (TCD), ordained 1849. Appointed Chaplain to the asylum on its opening. He resigned in 1860 to become Principal, Victoria College School, Vancouver, 1862-1870, and then Archdeacon of Holy Trinity Cathedral, Vancouver, B.C.

8   Edward returned to Leamington College to enter on his last term.

12   Called Wroxall. Mrs Claridge quite failing.[61]

15   Julie's birthday. She went in today for her second ambulance exam. [illegible] my sister Mary £20.

18   At a meeting of the Committee of the Asylum it was unanimously agreed to give me in place of my second Assistant Medical Officer a Deputy Superintendent, to relieve me of more of the detail of management at a salary of £350 p.a. with furnished accommodation, lighting, firing, washing & vegetables.[62]

22   Finally arranged by letter for my old A.M.O. Dr Herbert RO Sankey[63] to become my Deputy Superintendent. Mrs Jane Holbeche[64] who had been staying with us for

---

61   This was to be WHP's final visit to Mrs Claridge. She died on 31 May 1882, a 'widow of William Claridge, farm labourer'. Cause of death was 'Spinal affection & neuralgia ophthalmia 2 years (a neurological disorder of the spine and optic nerves, akin to MS in its behaviour, and which accounts for her 'partial blindness'); exhaustion 3 months'. The certificate was signed by Dr John Clarke MRCS, LSA, a general practitioner practicing in Kenilworth. It may have been that, in her last weeks, WHP and Dr Bullock transferred her medical care to him, as he lived much closer to Stoneleigh, when the frequency of visits, necessary when caring for the dying at home, increased.

62   The new Deputy MS would receive the same benefits in kind as did the MS, but without the 'feed for one horse'.

63   Dr Herbert RO Sankey MB (London), MRCS; he had been AMO at Hatton in 1876, and at the time of his appointment as Deputy MS was AMO at the County Asylum, Manchester. He became MS on WHP's death, but resigned five years later to take over the running of Boreatton Park, on the death of his father, Dr WHO Sankey.

64   Jane Holbeche, aged 69; lived with her sisters Sarah (77), Helen (59), Frances (56), a cook and a housemaid, at 20 Northgate Street, Warwick, (one of the finest Georgian streets

last few days left.
25 Called at Wroxall Abbey.
28 Called at Haseley Hall.

June
1 Julie succeeded in her ambulance 2nd certificate.[65] Dined with the Heaths.
5 To London. At Bessy's.[66]
9 London to Southsea. Harriet's.[67]
17 Southsea to London.
19 Home.
22-3 Dr Sankey with us for the day.
24 Leamington College cricket match.[68] Mr Owen[69] about a tutor for Edward in holidays.
28 Q[uarter]ly committee at Asylum confirmed arrangements for my Deputy Superintendent.
29 Called at Wroxall Abbey.
30 Thirtieth anniversary of opening of the Asylum.[70]

July
3 Julia to the Heaths.
7 Dined at the Heaths; Julia returned with us.

---

in the Midlands), on 'income from dividends', according to 1881 census.
65 According to the Leamington Spa Courier Certificates were awarded to 120 successful candidates by the St John's Ambulance Association.
66 See 28.
67 Sister Harriett (b 1819), married Charles Coward of 'no occupation', and was living at East Street, Fareham, Hants., with daughters Maud (23) and Louise (21), at the time, according to 1881 census.
68 Edward is not listed as playing for the College's cricket 1st XI.
69 Unidentified, very probably a master at Leamington College.
70 See 26.

8　Edward with Millington at home for the afternoon and evening.[71]

10　Called at Mrs Mulloy's.[72]

19　Dr Patrick E Campbell my senior Assistant Med. Off. left to take similar post at Caterham.[73]

26　Edward left Leamington College. Had been there since 1876. For the previous [blank space] was a boarder at the College preparatory school.

August

1　Luncheon at Coventry given by Dr Dewar,[74] president to the members of the Birmingham & Midland Counties Branch of British Med: Assoc:[75] after lunch visited the churches & other antiquities of Coventry. A very pleasant gathering.

12　Edward & Julie started for Westmoreland (Shap Wells

71　Regrettably, Millington remains stubbornly unidentifiable: presumably he was a Leamington College school friend of Edward's.

72　Unidentified.

73　Dr Patrick Edward Campbell MB (Edin.), MS; appointed MS to the Metropolitan Imbecile Asylum, Caterham, Surrey. Designed to accommodate 1560 patients, it opened in 1870, and was known as 'The Imbecile Colony'. Later renamed Caterham Mental Hospital in the 1930s. One block survives, converted to housing.

74　Dr Edward Dewes MD (Glasgow), MRCS, in practice at 1 The Quadrant, Coventry.

75　British Medical Association was founded in 1832 as the 'Provincial Medical & Surgical Association' at Worcester Royal Infirmary by Dr Charles Hastings, a general practitioner in the city (knighted 1850) and fifty other doctors, amongst whom was Dr John Conolly (then in practice in Warwick). Renamed BMA in 1855, it remains the professional body representing doctors and their interests in the UK. Recognised as a trade union in 1974.

Hotel)[76] with the Heaths.

Myself at the public luncheon given in the Pump Room,[77] Leamington, to Members of the British Med: Assoc: for Worcester

15 Dined at the Priory.[78]

20 Our old friend Miss Holbeche[79] of Warwick found dead in her bed at 7.30 this morning *aet* 78.

21 Dined at "The Lawn"[80] this evening to meet our former mutual friend Archdeacon Woods (our first chaplain) and Mrs Woods now staying in this country, from British Columbia.

Called at Mrs Mulloy's.

22 Dined at Emscote Parsonage (Rev Dr Dickins);[81] again met the Woods.

---

76 Shap Wells Hotel, a fine hotel at Shap, nr Penrith, Cumbria, and still in existence as such.

77 'Royal Pump Room', Leamington; built in 1814, to provide treatment in twenty baths for the many patients who visited when the town had a reputation as a spa (the waters – which are saline and taste ghastly – also have a mild laxative effect, so 'taking the waters' internally was encouraged by the town's physicians). It struggled financially when spa treatments became unfashionable, but was bought by a group of prominent townspeople led by Dr Jephson, who had been referring patients to the Pump Rooms since 1823. Today it is an art gallery, museum and recital hall.

78 Priory House, Warwick; built in 1566 (with much later redesign) on the site of a priory destroyed by Henry VIII. Demolished in 1926 (but rebuilt, retaining much of the interior, as 'Virginia House' in Richmond, Virginia, USA). Probably owned by the Wise family at the time (Christopher & Henry Wise were both founder members of the Leamington Tennis Court Club – see Afterword). Reason for WHP's dining there is not known.

79 See 65.

80 Residence of the Nelson family.

81 Rev Thomas Bourne Dickins received the degree of LL.D (Doctor of Law) from Cambridge University in 1882.

September

2   Edward & Julie returned from Westmoreland; have in the last two weeks seen much of the best scenery of the Lake District.

5   Dr Sankey entered on his duties as my Deputy Superintendent.

11 Myself went to stay with the Heaths for their last week in Westmoreland (Shap Wells Hotel). A splendid day, distances very clear; got a remarkably fine view from the highest ground above the Oxenholme station[82] where I had to wait 40 minutes. The furthest part of N Lancashire; Kendal at my feet; Langdale Pikes in N.W. distance.

12 With Mr & Mrs Heath & Hy Blenkinsop[83] for the day to Ullswater near Penrith. While on the lake hazy but on the return in the distance mountains illuminated by a peculiar pale silvery light from the sun through the mist. The effect striking.

13 Drove in the morning to Lower Borrowdale bridge; Mr H, Hy B, Lucy B, Isabel, Mabel & Alice H & Miss Fisher.[84] Intended to ascend the mountains and picnic on the top. Steady rain for an hour and a half; stopped the ascent. Drove to Tebay station, got our lunch there & drove homewards. At Orton again generally clear and fine. Mr H, Hy B & myself left the wagonette and walked up to the

---

82 Oxenholme station; on Lancaster & Carlisle Railway Co.'s route, south of Shap. The station served Kendal, with a branch line to Windermere.

83 Henry Blenkinsop (b 1854); younger brother to Lucy Blenkinsop (see 5); both children of Margaret Maxwell Heath, wife of Richard Child Heath (see 15) from her first marriage to Henry Blenkinsop (1813-1866), solicitor, and partner of Richard Child Heath.

84 Richard Child Heath, Henry Blenkinsop (stepson), Lucy Blenkinsop (stepdaughter), Isabel (14), Mabel (12), Alice (10), all daughters, and Marianne Fisher, servant (aged 16).

top of Orton Scar[85] 1350ft above sea level then across the ridge to Black Dub[86] on the moors, thence to Hotel. About 3 hours delightful scrambling walk. Put up several grouse.

14 Continuous wet. Read Darwin[87] on worms – chess, billiards & whist.[88]

16 Started for Shap station at 7.30am for Derwentwater near Penrith. Rain and mist on our journey. A splendid 5 hours at Derwentwater & Borrowdale mostly bright sunshine and plenty of cumulus cloud. Drove from station to Lodore Hotel.[89] Saw the waterfall[90] while a

85 Orton Scar; beautiful and unusual limestone pavements with an impressive view. WHP would have been delighted.

86 Black Dub; there is a monument on the summit to King Charles ll, who rested his army here in 1651 on his return from Scotland, where he had been crowned at Scone on 1 January. He was to be defeated by Cromwell at the Battle of Worcester in September, fleeing to France until his restoration in 1660.

87 Charles Darwin (1809-1892); naturalist and author. Published 'On The Origin of Species' in 1859, in which he proposed 'natural selection', or survival of the fittest, as a theory of evolution. By about 1870, Darwin's theory had been accepted as fact by most of the scientific world and by the public at large. Dissenters remained, however, mostly clergy, with the occasional scientist, such as Sir Richard Owen (1804-1892), Conservator of the Hunterian Museum, Royal College of Surgeons, who, in later life, became a fierce critic of Darwin.

88 No better way to spend a wet day indoors in the Lake District. However, had WHP been a keen climber, and staying in the Wasdale Head Inn, the usual amusement on wet days was for guests to make a circuit of the recreation room via the furniture and mantelpiece without touching the floor – in hobnailed climbing boots.

89 Lodore Hotel, nr Grange in Borrowdale; opened in 1870; a fine hotel and a popular venue in Victorian times (and since) for refreshment for tourists visiting Borrowdale and Derwentwater.

90 Lodore waterfall on Watendleth beck is in the grounds of

wagonette was getting ready. Drove to the head of Borrowdale. Examined the Bowder Stone about 2000 tons supported on its keel.[91]Lunched at the Hotel. Drove back to Keswick & home by rail. The day was remarkably suited for displaying the beauties and grandeur of the lake and all its surroundings. Our party Mr Heath, Lucy B, Miss Fisher, the three girls & myself. Skiddaw and Saddleback stood out very boldly.

15 [last two days transposed in diary] Drove in the morning to High Barrow Bridge over the Shap Fells ridge thence ascended a beautiful ridge about 1600f with bold broken summit, very picturesque; walked along about 3 miles and back. Saw some very fine pieces of rock scenery. The distance which should have been a fine vista now obscured by mist. Our party the same as for Derwentwater. Little Alice not equal to the walk & Lucy B stayed with her at the foot.

17 Sunday. Early morning wet. Later in the day & again in the afternoon walked on the moors.

18 The whole party returned to Warwick; after to me a very enjoyable week.

20 My old friend Rev Dr Dickins & Mrs Dickins gave me a handsome small clock and aneroid in return for supposed special attention during Mrs D's illness.[92]

---

the Lodore Hotel, and has been a popular destination for Lakeland tourists since Victorian times.

91 Bowder stone: thought at the time to be a glacial erratic (but now considered not), it still remains a Lakeland attraction, appearing, as it does, to be precariously balanced on one corner. Keen rock climbers continue to attempt to traverse its circumference (no mean feat).

92 WHP is being very modest, as ever. The episode of illness (judging from the increased frequency of WHP's visits) seems to have been from 26 April-4 May, but the actual diagnosis and treatment remain unknown. Presumably it must have been of

October

2   Went with Julia and Edward to London (Betsy's).

4   Went with Edward to Cambridge to enter him at St
     Peter's College.[93] By the courtesy of Mr Dickson
     (Mathematical Tutor) had rooms in the College until
     the 6th and dined with him & the Dean on the 4th & 5th.

6   Left Edward completely settled on the 6th returning to
     town to my sister Betsy's.

16   From London with Julia to Southsea (my sister
     Harriet's). When at Southsea saw many of the troops
     return from Egypt – landed at Portsmouth dockyard. As
     a body they appeared thin, worn and out of condition.[94]

November

3   Returned home from Southsea – during our visit much
     wet & unsettled weather with one very severe gale. Julia
     on the whole not been in good health: but the whole
     outing very enjoyable to both of us.

17–24 Pictures in the dining room and dressing room

---

        psychological origin, else her family doctor would have dealt
        with it without referral. It may well be that she had a relapsing
        depressive or bipolar illness that required periods of increased
        observation. WHP received gifts from other grateful patients
        or their families; one item of correspondence to this effect,
        together with a handful of merely administrative letters
        which WHP wrote on 'WCLA' headed notepaper, are the sum
        of the very sparse collection of WHP's personal papers which
        survive, apart from this diary.

93   Now known as Peterhouse, Cambridge.

94   This observation refers to British troops who had been
      involved in the second Anglo-Egyptian War. The British
      army invaded the Suez Canal Zone in August 1882 to protect
      it and maintain the canal route for British shipping and her
      commercial interests in India. A British presence remained in
      Egypt and controlled access to the Suez Canal until 1952.

cleaned and restored.[95]

29 The Dickins', Heaths, Nelsons, Sankeys, Dr Wilson & Mrs Wilson dined with us. Miss Dickins took her place.[96]

December

5 First day of Edward's 'Previous Examination' at Cambridge. Notice of purchase for me of £500 Reading Corp. shares on 11.11.

9 (Saturday). A most inclement week. Very heavy rains in the south, deep snow in the North last Sunday followed by the deepest general snow since the great fall in January 1881. Continued more or less through the week with alternating frost and partial thaw. Barometer below 29 inches all this week until yesterday when [it] began slightly to rise. There has been loss of life and stoppage of telegraph connections and transport up in many parts of the Northern Counties & Wales.
Edward returned this week from Cambridge.

20 Edward in the official list of those who had passed the 1st part of the Previous Exam: at Cambridge.[97]

---

95 Presumably in his personal accommodation.

96 Among the guest were Dr George Wilson MD (Edinburgh), MS, in practice at 22 Claremont Road, Leamington, and his wife. 'Miss Dickins' was the Dickins' daughter, Gertude Amelia.

97 'Previous Examination', (known colloquially as 'Little Go'), was taken by Cambridge undergraduates shortly after admission to their respective colleges. The exam consisted of questions on Latin, Ancient Greek and Mathematics. It was, in essence, a verification by the University of the academic standards of examinations of the many individual schools preparing students for admission.

1883

January

12 Season has thus far been remarkable for its mildness and rainfall. Yesterday the patients amusements were conducted within the Recreation Room without fires and with the windows open.

15 Edward returned to Cambridge. Julie to Stratford-on-Avon.[98]

23 Julia's birthday.[99] Gave her two enamel and gold hearts for [indecipherable].[100]

February

5 Thirty first anniversary of our wedding day.[101]
Duge to Southsea on a visit to her aunt Harriette.

26 Horse fell on Shank Hill. Beilby driving dragged off box, nose cut & grazed, forehead and lip cut slightly. Horse – hair partially off knees and slight cut over a fetlock.[102]

28 Duge returned from visit to Southsea.

March

11 A week of continuous severe frost with heavy snow showers: thaw during the heat of the day. On night of

---

98 Reason unknown.

99 The entry continues with a note about the transfer of £58.10 for (indecipherable) from (indecipherable) to Mrs Mary Ann Procter.

100 Regrettably the diary entry for this date is quite illegible; WHP gave his wife a birthday present of some form of jewellery, and then undertook more financial dealings on behalf of Mrs Mary Ann Procter.

101 See 15.

102 Driver of carriage was a Mr Beilby, who does not appear in the Register of employees of the asylum, but who may have been a member of the farm and garden staff.

8 – 9th the coldest of the week 13½ degrees of frost were registered against a very protected westerly aspect wall at 2½ feet from the ground. Each night since 9 degrees.

13 Edward returned from Cambridge.

25 Easter Sunday. Continuous winter weather since beginning of month. This morning 8 degrees of frost registered. Yesterday 9 degrees, on Thursday 11.

28 Wintery weather.

29 Much wind yesterday and rain last night & this morning, breaking up and fine spring afternoon. Mean temperature for the month from 2nd to 29th in this district 34.2: the lowest recorded in the last 38 years. The mean minimum reading 26.7; mean maximum 41.7.

April

3 My sixty-second birthday. My memory & capacity for continuous work scarcely as good as it might be and troubled still with insomnia; and as such very little sleep after 4am; otherwise in good health and activity and have passed my last year free from special anxieties or troubles.[103]

Ted going on very steadily at Cambridge.

11 & 12 Special theatrical performances for the patients on 11, for friends & neighbours on 12. "Don't judge by appearances" and "Prince Charming"[104] All the parts well sustained. Duge and Ted acted and sang very well. Large attendances.

14 Ted returned to Cambridge.

---

103 WHP was not to reach his 63rd birthday.

104 'Don't Judge by Appearances' & 'One of You Must Marry' have remained untraceable; quite possibly pantomimes written 'in house' by one of the asylum's staff. 'Prince Charming' is presumably a reprise of 'Cinderella' from 27 April the previous year.

On 6th forwarded to my brother-in-law & co-trustee Charles Coward 3 Beach Turn Southsea by GWR & SWR[105] one box containing deeds relating to the property (trust) in Drury Lane. Has acknowledged of receipt dated 8th (Sunday) received on 10th.

26 Signed preliminary contract for sale of 2/6 of before noted Drury Lane property as proposed by J A Brandon, solicitor, 21 Union St Portsea and returned same to him with my signature as arranged authority for him to release deposit.[106]

28 Forwarded to Mr Brandon at request of my co-trustee Charles Coward mortgage deed for £320 to us as trustees for him as owner of one of the 1/6th shares.

May

5 After inclement early May with cold showers and occasional sleet the ground this morning 8am covered with snow.

16–23 Myself to London staying at my sister Mrs Baker. Dined at Notting Hill; day at Fisheries Exhibition[107] day at Wimbledon.

23 Returned home, my sister Mrs Baker & my neice Lizzie[108] accompanying.

24–June 8 My sister Mrs Baker & Lizzie with us. Mrs Burman with us three days. Ellertons for the day: Hills[109](Leamington) ditto, Lucy Blenkinsop ditto. Tennis party at Heath's, Leamington, Warwick Castle

---

105 GW is Great Western Railway (founded 1833); SW is London & South Western Railway (founded 1838).

106 No further information available.

107 Fisheries Exhibition; this was a serious scientific piscatorial exhibition held in the grounds of Royal Horticultural Society in South Kensington between 12 May – 31 October.

108 Elizabeth W Baker (b 1864).

109 Unidentified.

etc.[110] Splendid weather for getting about the country; as it was during my time in London.

16 "Ted" came home from Cambridge.

Wrote on 13th to Chas Coward in reply to his letter regarding proceeds of sale of Drury Lane approaching completion, deed for which I signed as one of the trustees on 7[th.]

16 Heard from Cambridge that Ted had been successful in his exam.

25 Day at Stoneleigh camp.

30 Paid into Greenways Bank[111] £725 trust money under

---

110 The new game of lawn tennis had become very popular among middle class house owners (with a decent sized lawn) in the previous ten years, although it was still very much considered a game for 'girls and unathletic curates'. Major Thomas Henry ('Harry') Gem, a solicitor from Edgbaston and Juan Augurio Perera, a Spanish merchant, both rackets players, first played lawn tennis on Perera's lawn at 8 Ampton Road, Edgbaston, in 1865. In 1872, both men moved to Leamington, Gem to live at 21 Portland Place (where he died on 4 November 1887) and Perera in Avenue Road, opposite the Manor House Hotel. Together with two physicians from the Warneford Hospital, Dr Haynes (see 47) and Dr Arthur Tompkins MB (TCD), LRCS, MD – another member of Victorian Warwickshire's Trinity mafia – they formed the Leamington Lawn Rackets Club and played together on the lawn of the Manor House Hotel ('high Victorian gothic, rather grim' according to Pevsner; now luxury apartments). Gem wrote the first rules of the new game of 'Lawn Rackets or Pelota; the rules and laws of the game as played at the Leamington Club', in 1875 for the new club, which was the first lawn tennis club in the world. WHP's involvement in tennis, aged 62, would almost certainly have been confined exclusively to that of spectator.

111 Greenways Bank was a Warwick bank, with a branch in Leamington from 1863. It was founded in 1791 by Thomas

Mr C J Coward's will.

July 18–20 To Boreatton[112] to spend nineteenth with the Sankeys, stopping at Knowle to pass afternoon & evening with Julia, Julie & Ted at the Burmans.[113]

August

26–28 To Scarborough with Julia, Ted & Julie – first night at M A Procter's, remainder of time in lodgings. Lucy Blenkinsop with us [illegible]. A thoroughly enjoyable visit to all of us.

September

4   Called at Greenways Bank [...][114].

9   Daniel Reason (aet 35) Charge Attendant in the Asylum fell down and died while talking to a fellow attendant

---

Whitehead, a Quaker from Barford, the Greenway family becoming involved from about 1824. Dubious banking practices by the Greenways in the 1870s led eventually to its failure in 1887, causing much distress locally.

112   Boreatton Park, Baschurch, nr Shrewsbury; a mansion built in 1857, standing in 250 acres. Bought by Dr William Henry Octavius Sankey MRCS, LSA, in 1882, and became a 'licenced house for the reception of insane persons of the upper class'. He had previously been Physician to the Female Department at Hanwell Asylum and was an intimate friend of Conolly, during his last years of association with the asylum. After his death in 1889, his elder son Herbert Richard Octavius Sankey resigned as MS at Hatton to take over the running of Boreatton. On his death in 1894, his younger brother, Edward Hugh Octavius Sankey MB, BChir (Cantab), became proprietor, until it ceased to function as an asylum in the 1930s.

113   See 60.

114   The reason for the visit to the bank was regarding the £7825 trust money and related legal documents thereof, but the diary entry is indecipherable.

at about 8.45 in the morning. A worthy fellow and excellent attendant: his wife and sister all in the service of the asylum.[115]

10–12 My neice Mirrie Parmeter came from Southsea to say goodbye before she goes to St Helena.[116]

27–October

1 Julie is staying with the Sankeys at Boreatton.

2–9 Julia an invalid & confined to bed greater part of week.
Edward yesterday returned to Cambridge.
Today Mirrie Parmeter sails for St Helena.

20 Julia continues an invalid. Has had much obscure gastric disturbance. Partially recovered but gains strength very slowly.
Gales of unusual violence this past week.
Today invested £570 in Birmingham Corporation 3½ pc stock on 3 months notice.

24 While sitting at dinner at the Heaths (Myton Grange) Julia suddenly fainted. Came round slowly [underlined]; has fainted occasionally during her life after too active exertion in great heat & once nearly so on a similar

---

115 Daniel Reason (b 1847), lived with his wife, Ruth, and their two small children, Sarah (6) and Edith (3), at 6 Birmingham Road, Budbrooke. His elder sister Emma (b 1841) was a Head Attendant at the Asylum.

116 WHP's neice, Mary ('Mirrie') Elizabeth Parmeter, daughter of his youngest sister Mary Ann. Reason for her visiting St Helena is not known; it may be she was going to teach for a time in one of the island's schools. However, by 1891 she had returned to the UK, was boarding with a family in Maldon, Essex, and 'living on own means', according to the 1891 census. She died a spinster on 24 August 1940, aged 80, as a result of injuries sustained due to damage to her house in Southsea from a German bombing raid the previous night.

occasion to this.

31 Julia returning satisfactorily to her usual health

November
6–12 Julia on a visit to the Heaths, Myton Grange.[117]

December
5   My neice Maud Coward came on a visit for Xmas.
8   Edward returned from Cambridge.

This was to be Henry Parsey's final entry in the diary: he died, in the asylum, on 10 January 1884.

---

117 The Heaths were brave to invite her back, after the last episode.

AFTERWORD

During his years as Medical Superintendent of the Hatton asylum, Henry Parsey appears to have acquired a social circle that included a number of well known professional Warwickshire families, but he certainly didn't ignore more mundanely occupied local inhabitants or the elderly and more socially isolated.

This was to be expected, for references to his personal character universally describe a modest, charming intelligent man and a conscientious physician, concerned for the welfare of his patients and staff. No doubt his wife and children expressed much the same sort of character, for they were evidently well received at their social gatherings.

It is probable however that, in the South Warwickshire of the latter half of the 19C., the pinnacle of social acceptance would have been membership of the Leamington Tennis Court Club in Bedford Street, Leamington, which had been formed in 1846 by Lord Brooke (heir to the Earl of Warwick, who had provided the land for the new asylum) and nineteen other titled gentlemen or 'esquires' and – unusually for the time, for within the Club professional occupations were considered anathema – Dr Henry Jephson MD. He had been, though, steadily acquiring a considerable fortune from his fashionable Leamington practice during the years of the town's popularity in the first half of the century as a spa, having specialized in the diseases of the rich.

He lived with his wife Eliza at 'Beech Lawn', a twenty roomed house with three and a half acres of grounds in Warwick Street, Leamington (now the site of the Leamington Fire Station), with seven servants, a butler, a footman, a cook/housekeeper and lady's maid.

John Ruskin, art critic and the first Slade Professor of Fine Art at Oxford stayed in the town whilst consulting him, as did many other notable patients. However, to be fair, he was apparently a kindly man, and did treat many of his less well-off patients *gratis*, and often arranged treatment for them in the Pump Rooms.[1] Henry Parsey was a member of the Warwick Natural History & Archaeological Society, founded by Conolly, as were some members of the Tennis Court Club, but reciprocal membership was not so easily obtained; Tennis Court Club membership was available almost exclusively to gentlemen 'of no occupation' with private means, (apart from the good Dr Jephson), and election was achieved only after the proposed candidate had successfully negotiated the hazard of the black ball in the secret election process of the existing membership.[2]

According to Tennis Court Club legend, 'a local doctor, and a leading member of the profession', was blackballed by an earl, on the grounds that he (the earl) 'would not wish to meet someone socially who he might have to call in to visit him in the morning'.[3] That being the case, for such a member of the Tennis Court Club to be found engaged in conversation, in the Club, with the Medical Superintendent of the local lunatic asylum would have been, almost certainly, beyond the bounds of contemplation. (Dr W G Grace had similar difficulties obtaining membership of MCC, for very much the same reason).

However, be that as it may, Henry Parsey seems to have survived this misfortune, if it can be so described, without, one would assume, any loss of his usual equanimity, and plainly continued to enjoy his own social milieu.

Interestingly, the Blenkinsop, Heath and Nelson family names do not feature in the surviving membership lists of the Tennis Court Club until 1957, when all three names first appear.[4] Evidently, there was a world elsewhere.

What do the diary entries reveal to us of the man? His recreational interests in the natural world, which were very much those of the Victorian gentleman, at a time when Darwin and the study of the natural world had caught the public imagination were, no doubt, a satisfying – if singular – interest. His concerns and anxieties for his family, especially for their health in a pre-antibiotic era, (remembering he had had three children die in infancy or childhood in quick succession in seven years, and his wife Julia's health appears to have been quite fragile), and for his two surviving children's general welfare and academic progress, which he might otherwise have left unexpressed, are understandable, but these are, for the most part, very much those of any concerned husband and parent.

Are we expecting too much from a small diary's contents, written with no wider audience in mind? Probably. We must just be satisfied with the vignette it affords us of the day-to-day activities and concerns of a conscientious provincial Victorian medical man, who had 'decided to make lunacy his life's work'.[5]

Henry Parsey was a practicing Anglican, conducting daily prayers each morning in the asylum, and regularly reading a lesson at services in the chapel. He would no doubt have been familiar with John Keble's hymn 'New every morning', and concurred with Keble's sentiments expressed therein:

The trivial round, the common task,
Will furnish all we ought to ask;
Room to deny ourselves; a road
To bring us daily nearer God. [6]

ENDNOTES

1. A medal struck in his honour in 1848, on the opening of the town's 'Jephson Gardens', describes him as 'Henry Jephson Esquire MD"; which explains everything.
2. This method of electing new members was finally abolished in the 1930s; in 2011, ladies were finally admitted to the club as full members (although they had always been allowed in the premises, as guests, albeit under sufferance).
3. Wade *Leamington Tennis Court Club 1846-1996* p5.
4. Some ten years later, only two members of the Nelson family remained on the list of members; the exclusivity of the Club must not have suited everyone's temperament.
5. Royal College of Physicians obituary.
6. From *'New every morning'*, a hymn written in 1822 by John Keble (1792-1866), Anglican priest, poet and hymn-writer.

CHAPTER 9

DEATH IN OFFICE

Henry Parsey died at the Asylum on 10 January 1884, after a brief illness; he was aged 62. The last entry in his diary had been made just over 4 weeks earlier.

By the end of December 1883, just before his death, he had admitted and treated in the asylum more than 1350 patients (see Appendix 6).

The cause of death on his death certificate was given as:

Albuminuria; [a sign of failing kidney function]
Bronchopneumonia 7 days;
Weak Heart
(signed) W Thursfield MD.

His death certificate was signed by the Parsey family's doctor, Dr William Thursfield, and states Edward was present at the death. His wife Julia and daughter Julie must also have been present too, of course. Edward had not returned to Cambridge after the Christmas break, so it is likely that Henry Parsey must have had early signs of illness perhaps even before Christmas and certainly early in the New Year: the cause of death is suggestive of progressively worsening heart failure and declining kidney function as a consequence of a severe myocardial infarct (heart attack), probably occurring some time within the previous four weeks, with pneumonia as the terminal illness; regrettably, still a common course of events.

His death was greatly lamented. The BMJ obituary of 19 January commented:

> *Dr Parsey had been in charge of the large asylum at Hatton for many years, where his management was marked by signal success. He was extremely popular with all classes...*

It also carried the following letter in the same edition:

> *SIR – May I be allowed, through the medium of your columns, to pay a tribute of respect to the memory of the late Dr W. H. Parsey, who, for upwards of thirty years, had been the Medical Superintendent of the Warwick County Asylum at Hatton?*
>
> *My testimony, as that of a layman who has been on intimate terms with him for the last thirty-three years, who worked with him from 1850 to 1853 at the Devon Asylum, under the direction of Dr J.C. Bucknill, F.R.S. (still, happily, with us), and who has since had ample opportunities of forming a just estimate of his worth, will not, I trust, be rejected even if the means I adopt may be an unusual one in your paper.*
>
> *Medical directories and professional registers record Dr. Parsey's technical qualifications, and point to the good work he has done, but they can say nothing, as I can, of his clear judgment, unwearied industry, enlightened humanity, unswerving integrity, and unselfish life. He had all these qualities to the full, but he was essentially not a "showy" man; his metal was too pure for that.*
>
> *How often, in the last thirty years or so, when in doubt, have I put the question to myself, "What would Dr Parsey do under like circumstances?" That point once settled I felt safe, nor have I any reason to regret my faith, for his aim was ever to act righteously.*
>
> *He passed away at Hatton, on Wednesday last, the 10th inst., somewhat suddenly, inflammation of the lungs and other*

*complications being the cause. He leaves a widow, a son, and a
daughter.*

> *"To live in hearts we leave behind
> Is not to die"*

> *I am, sir, your obedient servant,
> Geo H Haydon
> Bethlem Royal Hospital, S.E.*

George Haydon had left the Devon Asylum in 1853 (where
he had also been a member of Bucknill's 'Exeter & South
Devon Volunteers') to become Steward of Bethlem &
Bridewell Hospitals, in which post he remained for thirty
six years until his retirement in 1889, although he had
maintained a friendship, as seen from the diaries, with
Henry Parsey until the latter's death.

The same quotation that ends the above letter adorns
his own gravestone.[1]

The Journal of the Royal College of Physicians noted:

> *...[Dr Parsey's] life's work began with his nomination as
> superintendent of the new County Asylum at Hatton, Warwickshire.
> Under his supervision the Asylum more than doubled in size and
> achieved a world-wide reputation. Parsey himself, who followed the
> 'non-restraint' methods of Conolly, was loved by his patients and
> highly respected by the local magistrates. Outside the county he was
> considered a leading authority on his subject...*

And 'W. J. S.' who had worked under him for a time, wrote
in the British Journal of Psychiatry:

> *With his patients, his relations were of a cordial nature, his kindness
> and goodness of heart conspicuous; and great were his forbearance*

and tact in dealing with many difficult cases, and never-wearying his thoughtfulness and assiduity in making provision for their better interests and care and cure.

To those who worked under him in any capacity he showed a generous kindness and benevolence of disposition, mingled with a firmness, which made his rule at once successful and agreeable. A considerate or indulgent bearing towards the various members of the staff, however, never relaxed into looseness of control, or permitted of carelessness in duty.

He will long live in the memories and affections of all those who were privileged to know him. His friendships were intimate and cordial. They who knew him best loved him best.

Finally, Edward Moreland Parsey's letter to Dr Stern (then Medical Director), written in 1952, regarding the Asylum's proposed Centenary celebration also contained the following, originally printed in the *Lancet*, copied by the Leamington Spa Courier, 26 January 1884:

IN MEMORIAM-On January 10th there passed away from us a man little known perhaps to the rising generation of medical men, but one who was well-known to those of his own, and one who was a very dear and valued friend of all those who had the privilege of his more intimate acquaintance.

No man was better known to all who are worth knowing in the County of Warwick and no man more esteemed. To his professional brethren he was ever kind, courteous and a wise counsellor, whilst his opinion in his special branch was highly estimated.

In his death our profession has lost one of its many noble characters, such as exist, we know unrecognized by the world at large, but known only in their full beauty to their intimate friends. Psychological medicine has lost one of its skilled experts and his friends have lost one who will long live in their memories and never be wholly replaced.

*

Henry Parsey's funeral took place at Holy Trinity Church, Hatton, and was conducted by the Chaplain to the Asylum for the previous twenty four years, the Rev Dr Thomas Dickins.[2]

His body lies interred in the churchyard, on the right of the path to the North entrance to the Church.

A notice appeared in the BMJ on 10 January 1885: exactly 12 months to the day since his death:

THE LATE DR W H PARSEY

A HANDSOME and massive tomb has just been placed in Hatton churchyard, to the memory of the late HENRY PARSEY, for upwards of thirty years medical superintendent of the Warwickshire County Lunatic Asylum, at Hatton. The tomb is of Inverness granite, with landing and moulded base of Yorkshire stone, and it has been erected by the officers, committee of management, attendants, and others connected with the asylum.

And a very fine tomb it is. Along the tomb's length on the left, is inscribed:

TO THE PIOUS MEMORY OF W. H. PARSEY ESQ B. A. M. D.
FELLOW OF THE ROYAL COLLEGE OF PHYSICIANS
(LONDON)
AND FOR 32 YEARS MEDICAL SUPERINTENDENT
OF THE WARWICK COUNTY ASYLUM

And along its length on the right:

THIS MONUMENT IS ERECTED BY
THE OFFICERS, ATTENDANTS, COMMITTEE OF
VISITORS
AND OTHERS CONNECTED WITH THE INSTITUTION

HE DIED AT THE POST OF DUTY JANy 19th 1884
AGED 62 YEARS +

A small inscription to William George Parsey is placed on the left end of the crosspiece of the tomb: but there are no references to the two girls who died in childhood.

After his death, his widow Julia moved from the asylum to a house in King's Norton, where she was to remain until her death, aged 74, on 9th July 1896. She must have been nursed in her final illness by Julie and Edward to a very great degree, for Edward was to sign her death certificate (and therefore must have been in attendance within the previous 14 days).[3]

Her funeral on nineteenth July was also conducted at Hatton church by the Rev Dr Dickins. She was laid to rest with her husband in the churchyard, and the following inscription was added to the tombstone:

HERE
ALSO
LIE THE
MORTAL
REMAINS
OF
JULIA, WIDOW OF W. H. Parsey M.D.
ENTERED INTO REST July 9th 1896, AGED 74

Julia Mary ('Julie') continued to live in her mother's house in King's Norton, describing herself in the 1901 census as 'of independent means', and never married. Some years later, she placed a memorial stained glass window to both her parents, in one of the windows on the North side of the church at Hatton.

She died on 6 March 1928 in her mother's house and is also buried in the churchyard of Hatton church.

After Dr Parsey's demise, Edward returned to Cambridge, graduating BA in Natural Sciences, as his father had done, in 1885. He went on to graduate MA in 1892. This degree was – and still is – something of a 'long service and good conduct medal', which is awarded on request, for a – surprisingly modest – fee, to any BA graduate of Oxford, Cambridge or Trinity College, Dublin, 'of three years good standing', (ie without a criminal record). A not particularly onerous requirement.

Edward entered St Thomas's Hospital for his clinical medical training, and graduated MB, B Chir (Cantab) in 1894. Exactly what he did in the years between his graduating BA in 1885 and entering St Thomas's is not known, apart from a single documented appearance in amateur dramatics in 1887. However, after qualification he spent six months as an Assistant Resident Medical Officer at Paddington Infirmary, which had opened in 1886.[4]

After Paddington Infirmary, he lived briefly at 40 High Street, Warwick, but by the time of his marriage he was in practice in King's Norton, in Worcestershire. He married Sara Janet Moreland (a nurse whom he had met at St Thomas's) on 15 May 1895 at St Mary's Church, Warwick, the service once again being conducted by the Rev Dr Dickins.

Whilst in general practice in King's Norton, It is known that he would occasionally take female patients into 'Glenavon', his family home on the Redditch Road: it is my suggestion that he may have been continuing the tradition of physicians taking selected (female) psychiatric patients into their home to live as one of the family, as Conolly had done at Lawn House, after his retirement from the Hanwell asylum, and as we have also seen Dr Dartnell to have done in Henley-in-Arden; it had become an increasingly common practice by the end of the nineteenth century as the standard of accommodation in asylums continued to deteriorate with the increasing numbers.

In any event, Edward continued in general practice in King's Norton for the rest of his life. Edward and Sara raised two children, Janet May and Edward Moreland, and he remained on the Medical Register until 1935, by which time he was aged 69.

Sara died the following year, but he survived until December 1944, when he too died, aged 80. Both Sara and he are buried in the churchyard of All Saints Church, King's Norton. Edward Moreland – known as 'Moreland' – became a barrister-at-law and continued to live on in 'Glenavon'.

ENDNOTES

1. The quotation is from the poem '*Hallowed Ground*' by Thomas Campbell (1777-1844); a Scottish poet, and co-founder of University College, London, who is buried in Poet's Corner, Westminster Abbey.
2. He had been awarded a DD (Doctor of Divinity) degree by Cambridge University in 1881.
3. A statutory requirement.
4. It was renamed Paddington General Hospital at the inception of the Health Service in 1948. My father was one of the hospital's pharmacists in the 1960s. It closed in 1985 and has been replaced by a block of flats.

CHAPTER 10

INTO THE 20ᵀᴴ CENTURY

After Dr Parsey's death, a successor as Medical Superintendent had to be found. It was probably a logical move for the Committee to appoint Dr Herbert Richard Octavius Sankey, whom Henry Parsey had approached personally in 1882 to join him as Deputy Superintendent.

But Herbert Sankey's father, Dr William Henry Octavius Sankey, was to die unexpectedly in 1889. He had been 'Physician to the Female Wing' at Hanwell Asylum for some years in the 1850s – where he had been a contemporary and friend of Conolly during his very last years as Visiting Physician – but had been running a private asylum 'licensed for the reception of insane patients of the upper classes' at Boreatton Park, in Shropshire, since 1882, which the Parseys had frequently visited, as can be seen from Henry Parsey's diary entries. Herbert Sankey was forced to resign as the Medical Superintendent at Hatton in 1891, to take over the running of Boreatton.

Regrettably, he was to die not many years after his father, in 1894, leaving his younger brother, Edward Hugh Octavius Sankey, a Cambridge graduate, to take over the asylum until it was eventually sold in 1930, to become an 'approved school'.[1]

★

The Committee's appointee as successor to Herbert Sankey was Dr Alfred Miller. Alfred Miller had joined Henry Parsey as an Assistant Medical Officer (after arriving somewhat unexpectedly at Hatton, as Henry Parsey commented in his diary) on 26 April 1882, but by the following year he was expected to leave Hatton, to very gracious praise from Dr Parsey, in that year's Annual Report:

Dr Miller's energy, good ability and kindly and willing disposition have made him one of the most useful and agreeable Assistant Medical Officers that in the course of many years I have had to work under me. I greatly regret that the Asylum is losing his services, though glad to be able to congratulate him on the change which will advance his position and prospects in the specialty in which my own professional life has been passed, and which he wishes to adopt as his permanent life's work.

His tombstone states he was Assistant Medical Officer for 10 years before taking up the post of Medical Superintendent in 1891, so he must have changed his mind about leaving Hatton after Henry Parsey's sudden death in 1884, for he continued at Hatton as the Senior Assistant Medical Officer until he succeeded Herbert Sankey.

Alfred Miller was an Irishman, born in Kingstown (now Dun Laoghaire), Co. Dublin on 1 July 1859, the second of five brothers. He qualified as a doctor from Trinity College, Dublin in 1881, as did his youngest brother William nine years later (whose career was spent as a GP in Penzance).

As a medical student, Alfred had played rugby for Kingstown FC, rather than the Trinity club (Dublin University FC), but played to a high enough standard whilst a medical student to be selected to represent Ireland in the 1879-80 'Home Nations' series of matches, playing against England at Lansdowne Road in January 1880 and against Scotland in Glasgow in February 1880.[2]

By 1883 he had graduated and was in post at the Asylum, and playing rugby for Leamington Rovers FC[3], when he was again selected – surprisingly – to play for Ireland against England in February 1883, at Whalley Range in Manchester, in the first 'Home Nations Championship'.[4]

(Another TCD medical student, Daniel Rambaut, who played for Trinity's DUFC whilst an undergraduate, also played for Ireland, in 1887 at Lansdowne Road – in a team which included Thomas Gisborne Gordon, the only one-handed player ever to play International rugby[5] – and converted the two tries that gave Ireland their very first victory over England in an International match.[6]

He later became a colleague and friend of Alfred Miller, when, after some years as Assistant Medical Officer at the Grangegorman Asylum in Dublin, he was appointed, in 1913, the Medical Superintendant at St Andrew's Hospital, Northampton, where he remained until his death in 1937).

★

Alfred Miller married Henrietta Hodson Morris, from Armagh, in Holy Trinity Church, Paddington, on 12 September 1895;[7] he was by then aged thirty six, she was aged twenty six and living in Dublin. They returned to Hatton and went on to have three daughters; Beryl, born in 1897, Dorothy in 1901 who died young, and Christabel Henrietta, also born in 1901. Beryl remained a spinster, but in June 1934 Christabel married John Bertie Margetts, of John Margetts & Son, the Valuers and Estate Agents in Warwick, and they had one daughter, Henrietta, born 1937, who died a spinster In 1999.

192

Alfred Miller also proved to be a highly conscientious Superintendent, was very well liked by both patients and staff, and did a great deal to improve the education and training of attendants and nurses.

In 1877 the St John's Ambulance Association had introduced a very popular course of first aid instruction followed by a practical examination and Alfred Miller introduced this into the asylum soon after his appointment as Medical Superintendent. He wisely introduced initially an assessment that was practical rather than written, and he included basic literacy and numeracy in his course of first aid lectures, which made the St John's certificate a very popular award among the attendants at Hatton.

Although Hatton had a long tradition of loyal and long-serving staff, mostly resident but including some some who lived in Warwick and the surrounding villages, whose children would often come to be employed by the asylum in turn, in asylums nationally there was quite a rapid turnover in staff – the average duration of stay being about two and a half years. It was thought that if attendants nationally were to be offered a training course followed by an assessment, with the award of a certificate of competence to the successful, then a small increase in pay as reward could be given, which might secure increased longevity of service.

To this end, The Medico-Psychological Association introduced a 'Handbook for the Instruction of Attendants on the Insane' in 1885, known universally as the 'Red Book'. It soon became the standard training manual and, regularly updated, was used in the training of psychiatric nurses until the 1970s.[8]

The Medical-Psychological Association then introduced a 'Certificate of Proficiency in Nursing' in 1891: candidates with two years experience of asylum nursing took both written and *viva voce* examinations, certificates awarded to the successful and a Register of those successful maintained by the Association. The Register required a Registrar, of course, who also administered the examinations. Dr Miller succeeded Dr Beveridge Spence of Lichfield, the first Registrar and continued in that post until his death, whereupon his colleague and Irish rugby International, Dr Daniel Rambaut, of St Andrew's, Northampton, succeeded him in turn.

Dr Rambaut wrote in his Annual Report to St Andrew's, Northampton, in 1928:

> *It is interesting to see the wonderful change that this training brings about in the Mental Nurse. The knowledge of anatomy, physiology, and mental illness and its treatment properly implanted, changed the prison warder, drill sergeant, and policeman type of attendant into the sympathetic, long-suffering skilled and tactful modern Hospital nurse.*[9]

There had plainly been considerable advances in recruiting and training attendants since the early years of the century, when the 1815 Parliamentary Enquiry were told of Bedlam's selection process:

> *attendants are chosen for their strength and sobriety, and the latter is often overlooked.*

And Conolly, on his arrival at Hanwell in 1838, discovered that the staffing level was four attendants to one hundred patients, and – in his opinion – some of the male attendants 'were not suited to be entrusted with the care of valuable dogs'.

Further innovation was to follow. It was whilst Alfred Miller was Medical Superintendent that the appointment of the first female Assistant Medical Officer, Dr Mary Victoria Littlejohn, was made. Women doctors were still few in number: they were considered too delicate for the rigours of medical school – one argument being that it was unseemly for women to attend anatomy classes, part of which took the form of teaching 'indecent mnemonics'.[10]

Mary Victoria Littlejohn had qualified at the University of Aberdeen in 1919, and was appointed AMO in 1921. Little is known about her medical career, except that by 1928 she was no longer in post in the asylum. She married a Leamington man, Sidney Flavel, in June 1936 and they lived in Leamington at 54 Warwick Place. She may have gone into general practice, for she was still living there and on the Medical Register in 1947. Her successor, also female, was Dr Florence Margaret Gamble, a London University graduate, who joined the asylum in 1928, but appears to have left when she married in 1936. She may have done the same, for she was still on the Medical Register in 1953, and living in London.

★

Alfred Miller remained in post for thirty two years, until his death on 4 December 1923. He died, aged 64, in the recently built Superintendent's House after a brief illness, whilst still Medical Superintendent, just as Henry Parsey had done before him. The cause of death on his death certificate was as follows:

Lymphadenoma (of uncertain duration)
Cardiac Failure
(signed) Henry Brougham Leech M.D.

Henry Brougham Leech, (elder brother of the more famous William[11]), was at that time AMO at the asylum. Their father had been Regius Professor of Law at Trinity College,

Dublin from 1888-1908, and Henry was yet another TCD medical graduate who joined the Hatton asylum: it must have had a recruiting officer outside Front Gate. He became Medical Superintendent in 1933, after 25 years as AMO, but only briefly: three years later he resigned to become the Medical Director of the Weston Colony for Mental Defectives which had opened in 1929 in a former boys' reformatory at Weston-under-Wetherley, near Leamington Spa.

It was a satellite of the asylum and a residential home for children with learning difficulties. One senses that perhaps the responsibilities of Superintendency of a large asylum did not suit his temperament, and he was happier administering a smaller establishment. However, by 1833, some four years later, he was living in retirement at 55 Kenilworth Road, Leamington, where he died in 1968, aged 88.[12]

★

Of Dr Miller's death, the Leamington Spa Courier reported on 7 December 1923:

> *Dr Miller had been prominently associated with the official life of the county, and his cheery nature made him a general favourite wherever he went.*
>
> *Occupying a peculiarly exacting and difficult post, he discharged his duties in a way that won him the regard of all who came in contact with him.*

An obituary was carried in the BMJ of 29 December 1923:

> *DR ALFRED MILLER, medical superintendent of the County Mental Hospital, Hatton, died on December 4th. He was educated at Trinity College, Dublin, and graduated M.B., B.Ch. in 1881. He had*

been connected with the asylum for about forty years, first as assistant medical officer and for thirty-four years as medical superintendent. He was also medical advisor to the County Mental Deficiency Act Committee, registrar of the Medico-Psychological Association of Great Britain and Ireland, and a member of the committee of management and house committee of the Warneford Hospital, Lamington. He was a keen sportsman and in his early life was an Irish international Rugby footballer. He is survived by his widow and two daughters.

A further brief notice was published in the BMJ the following week:

The Warwickshire Local Management Committee, representing upwards of 200 medical practitioners, desire to place on record their sincere regret for the death of Dr Alfred Miller, who for many years was Medical superintendent of the County Asylum. His marked administration ability and conscientious discharge of his multifarious duties won for him the high regard of all classes of the community, while his genial courteous manner and his ever-readiness to help endeared him to all his colleagues, who respectfully tender to Mrs Miller and her daughters sincere sympathy in their sad bereavement.

He too was buried in the churchyard of Holy Trinity Church at Hatton, in 'a grave lined with ivy and flowers, in a coffin of English oak'. Among the many mourners was Dr Daniel Rambaut, his fellow rugby International and colleague from St Andrew's Hospital, Northampton.

★

On visiting the churchyard, and walking some 30m from the south wall of the Chancel, there is an area which is given over to wild flowers and is providing a natural habitat. In this area, another tomb of Inverness granite 'erected by the Members of the Committee, Officers and Servants of the asylum' is to be found: that of Solomon Reason, Head Attendant for 24 years, who died on March 26th 1887, aged 42. His burial site is beneath a Yew tree, just at the edge of the area of wild flowers.

Dr. Miller's grave lies much deeper within the wild flower area near the perimeter wall of the churchyard, and is another tomb of Inverness granite, which bears the following inscription on the right hand side:

IN LOVED AND HONOURED MEMORY OF ALFRED
MILLER M. B.
WHOSE LIFE WAS DEVOTED TO THE WELFARE OF ALL
CONNECTED WITH THE WARWICK COUNTY MENTAL
HOSPITAL
OF WHICH HE WAS FOR 10 YEARS ASSISTANT MEDICAL
OFFICER
AND FOR 32 YEARS MEDICAL SUPERINTENDENT
BORN 4th AUGUST 1859 DIED 4th DECEMBER 1923

And on the left:

Blessed are the dead which die in the Lord, Yea saith the spirit that they May rest from their labours: and their works do follow them Rev XIV.13.

On a happier note, some years after his death, his daughters Beryl and Christabel donated to the Central Hospital (as the asylum was then known) a large carved wood panel in memory of their father. It had been made by R H Fyson, a cabinet maker and woodcarver of Kencot, near Lechlade, and it depicted many aspects of work and occupational therapy carried out by patients in the asylum.

On its installation in the chapel, the panel was dedicated by Canon Haydon, Vicar of St Mary's, Warwick, on 25 June 1961, and on the asylum's closure, it was reinstalled in the chapel of the new St Michael's Hospital.

ENDNOTES

1. It is now an outdoor adventure centre.
2. England won by one goal to nil; Scotland won by three goals to nil.
3. Leamington Rovers Rugby Football club was formed in 1876, a few years after the formation of the RFU in 1871. Their playing colours were black shirt with white skull & crossbones on the chest, and white (below the knee) shorts. Alfred Miller does not feature in team lists of club matches after 1883. The club folded in 1886, due to non-payment of subscriptions, but was reformed as Leamington RFC in 1926.
4. England won by one goal to nil.
5. Thomas Gisborne Gordon (1851-1935), solicitor, educated at Rugby School, played rugby for North of Ireland FC (NIFC) and as a three-quarter for Ireland three times, despite having previously lost his right hand in a shooting accident.
6. The final score was 6-0 to Ireland. The Irish fullback was Dolway Walkington who had poor eyesight and played wearing a monocle, removing it when required to make a tackle. He captained Ireland twice in 1888.
7. Demolished 1984.
8. Arton *Mental Health Nursing.*
9. £2 per annum was added to the pay of those nurses and attendants who successfully completed the course and examination.
10. Elston *Women Doctors in the British Health Services.*
11. William John Leech RHA (1881-1968); Irish impressionist painter.
12. The Weston Colony closed in the 1990s.

CHAPTER 11

DECLINE AND FALL

Overcrowding within the asylum had been a problem even since the early years. At the Centenary Celebrations in 1952, the Guest of Honour, Miss Pat Hornsby-Smith, Parliamentary Secretary to the then Minister of Health, Iain Macleod, planted a tree to mark the occasion, and in her speech, stated:

> *this hospital is rightly counted as one of the most progressive and up to date in all that concerns the active treatment of the mentally sick.*

She praised the staff and also made reference to the 'grave and difficult' problem of overcrowding. If it was thought to be 'grave and difficult' with 1392 inpatients in 1952, then the situation nearly ten years later was manifestly intolerable: by then the asylum was housing more than 1600 patients.

★

The introduction of anti-psychotic drugs in the 1950s had revolutionized therapeutics for the insane; medication was now available which produced a very great reduction in the psychotic symptoms of hallucination, delusion and physical violence, (today called 'challenging behaviour'), making the behaviour of such patients very much more amenable, so that, for the first time it was possible to discharge some

200

patients from the asylum and re-integrate them with family and friends. The aim of treatment then – as now – being 'to alleviate the suffering of the patient (and carers) and to improve social and cognitive functioning'.[1]

It soon became evident that to do this, many patients would require life-long medication (despite side-effects, some of which could be severe and some – rarely – irreversible). Unfortunately, no drug can have a desired pharmacological effect without having an undesired side-effect, but, be that as it may, it was still a very significant advance in therapeutics compared to what went before.

In spite of attempts to reduce overcrowding, the nation's patience had run out. In 1961, the Rt Hon Enoch Powell, the then Minister of Health, in what came to be known as his 'water-tower speech', indicated – without consultation – that the future care of the mentally ill must be in wards and wings of general hospitals, not in 'great isolated institutions.'

He proposed 'the elimination of by far the greater part of this country's mental hospitals as they exist today [...]. There they stand, isolated, majestic, imperious, brooded over by the gigantic water-tower and chimney combined, rising unmistakable and daunting out of the countryside – the asylums which our forefathers built with such immense solidity to express the notions of their day. If we err, it is our duty to err on the side of ruthlessness. For the greater majority of these establishments there is no appropriate future use.'[2]

The death knell had sounded for the asylums, although Hatton's final demise would not come for another forty years.

But Enoch Powell was right, of course: asylums in their present state could no longer be viewed as 'a blessed manifestation of true civilisation' – if they ever had been

– for the lives of patients requiring long-term care had become close to intolerable.

Enoch Powell had his way eventually, of course. By the 1990s most of the old asylum buildings in England had been demolished or fallen into dereliction and decay. But not all. A number still remain, 'isolated, majestic, imperious', transformed, like Hatton, and probably to Enoch Powell's fury, into luxury apartments. What was provided for the patients in their stead?

'Care in the Community' was going to substitute for the asylums, whereby mentally ill patients would be managed ('cared for' is possibly too strong a term) in small community based units, providing day care for very much the most part, with little provision of institutional care, although there would still be psychiatric beds, albeit far fewer in number, for inpatient care, which would, it was hoped, be of a significantly briefer duration.

The model proved to be erroneous, but was probably driven by an expectation that advances in medication would, with the passage of time, make support from social services and community psychiatric nurses even easier. Well meaning, of course, but even with the best will in the world from all those involved, the expected revolution did not follow. For support services such as clinical psychology, occupational therapy, and the various 'talking therapies' – effective if introduced early in the course of mental illness remain very stretched resources indeed: a waiting time for treatment measured in months is of very little benefit to anyone.

The major criticism of present day psychiatric care is that whilst there may be adequate provision of out-patient facilities, albeit somewhat fragmentary, there are few ways of supervising compliance with medication-taking – and none at all of enforcement – in the community, there are but few facilities for inpatient care and this applies to children and adolescents most acutely – especially if you are not being compulsorily detained in a psychiatric ward under the Mental Health Act, that is (and even then it may not always be possible to find a bed for you immediately).

It is a harsh observation to make, but it does seem to be an unforeseen consequence that there doesn't seem to be much continuity of 'care in the community'; if patients default meetings with social workers or outpatient appointments they can often slip through the net, deteriorate mentally and end up in either custodial care or homelessness.

The Victorian asylums may have gone forever – and rightly so, perhaps – but the Victorians model of provision of care for pauper lunatics was enlightened thinking for the age, and the nation's provision of mental health care since their demise could itself attract the criticism – to use Enoch Powell's phrase – of 'erring on the side of recklessness'.

★

It is regrettable that the Victorian alienists are frowned upon rather in the history of medicine: they are considered to have been poorly qualified for the task in hand, yet many were Licentiates of the Royal College of Physicians (by examination), and a number Fellows (by election). It is thought by some that their driving force was to build lucrative empires in the sub-specialty of psychological medicine, and that their governing body, the Medico-Psychological Association spent an inappropriate amount of time negotiating a satisfactory superannuation schemes for its members. But no doubt no more than many of the other similar professional bodies at the time.

It must be remembered that resident doctors in asylums were not particularly well rewarded financially in the nineteenth century, and, as has been noted, all asylum staff had to obtain permission to marry from the Medical Superintendent. It is quite possible that this might be refused, and therefore best not requested in the first place. Could the conversation which Wardle Bowen had with Dr Parsey, and which led to such catastrophic consequences, have been on such a topic?

The Victorian alienists appear to have been as dedicated and conscientious as any other contemporary medical man in any other specialty of the profession; Henry Parsey can rightly take his place alongside John Conolly and John Bucknill as one of the 'Three Notable Nineteenth Century Psychiatrists of Warwickshire'.

ENDNOTES

1. BNF 64 (2012); section 4.2.1
2. Rt Hon Enoch Powell: Speech & Nat. Assoc. for Mental Health 9 March 1961.

APPENDIX 1

COMMON DESIGNS FOR VICTORIAN ASYLUMS

The purpose-built asylum of the Victorian era was built to one of five designs:

* Radial design
  Five or six wards radiated from a central administrative block. It was an early design and lacked natural light, adequate circulation of air and decent sized airing courts. Only two were built to this design, one of which being the Devon County Lunatic Asylum.
* Corridor design
  A popular design throughout the nineteenth Century. A central administration block stood between two long corridors containing the wards. Sexes were easily segregated and staff could move around the wards quickly. Hatton Asylum and the Idiot Asylum were of this design, (as was Colney Hatch Asylum, with 1,200 beds, and the longest corridors in the country).
* Pavilion design
  Much like corridor design, but with smaller 'pavilions' at the end of each corridor, originally designed for epileptics and difficult cases.
* Echelon design
  Wards with corridors were 'staggered' from the central block, allowing good communication and were light

and airy for the patients, still segregated by sex, with views of the extensive grounds in which the asylum was situated. Designed originally by Dr Thomas Kirkbride, an alienist from Pennsylvania, many American asylums were based on the 'Kirkbride Plan'.

- Colony design
  By now the long corridors had disappeared, and wards were free-standing. Because staff movements were necessarily limited, this design was only adopted for smaller asylums.

APPENDIX 2

STRATFORD-UPON-AVON DISPENSARY: MEDICAL DETAILS OF THE FIRST 40 PATIENTS TREATED (1828)

Female 27	servant	dyspepsia
Female ?	widow	hydrops
Female 25	labourer's wife	dyspepsia
Female 35	labourer's wife	morbus uteri
Female 15m	servant's child	morbus cutis
Male 60	labourer	bronchitis
Female 57	nurse	ophthalmia
Male 71	labourer	internal derangement of knee
Male 46	nailer	hernia inguinalis
Female 49	servant's widow	rheumatismus
Female 25	servant's wife	necrosis of the tibia
Male 23	tailor	vomitus matutinus
Female 26	matcher's wife	fistula lachrimatis
Female 44	labourer's wife	dyspepsia
Female 14	servant out of place	dolor capitis
Female 68	widow	morbis cutis
Female 27	merchant's daughter	hypochondriasis
Male 50	labourer	hydrothorax
Female 7	labourer's daughter	abcessus
Female 70	labourer's wife	hysteria
Female 30	dressmaker	haemoptysis
Female 47	(none entered)	syphilis
Female ?	labourer's wife	ulcer of the toe

Female 14	labourer's daughter	scabies
Female 15	carpenter's daughter	tumour of the lip
Female 23	carpenter's wife	pleuritis
Female 57	maltster's wife	hepatitis
Male 3	labourer's child	convulsio
Female 33	schoolmistress	palpitatio hysterica
Female 45	labourer's wife	mania
Female 2	labourer's child	burns
Female 10	labourer's child	febris remittans infantum
Female 43	labourer	eruptio
Female 28	housekeeper	tussis
Female 21	labourer's wife	amaurosis (surg)
Male 21	housekeeper's son	phthisis
Male 15	schoolboy	epilepsia
Male 19	servant	lepra
Male 11	labourer's child	scabies
Female 66	widow	bronchitis

NOTES

1. Of the first 100 patients, 33 received a surgical diagnosis: the Dispensary was evidently providing 'medical and surgical advice and remedies to the sick poor', and was not just a convalescent home.
2. The first death in the Dispensary did not occur until the 133rd admission and was that of an 8 month old labourer's child, who had been admitted, on Conolly's recommendation, with 'sequelae rubeola' or 'complications of measles' – presumably measles pneumonia or encephalitis. Measles had a significant mortality rate in 1828.
3. The first forty patients treated show the usual mix of age (15 months to 71 years), medical illness (bronchitis; convulsions), surgical conditions (inguinal hernia), occupational disease (hepatitis in a maltster's wife – presumably of alcoholic

cause); infectious diseases (syphilis in a female patient, whose occupation is discreetly left blank in the register), florid mental illness (mania), anxiety-related disorders (palpitatio hysterica), and presumed domestic accidents (burns in a child), that constituted ordinary general medical practice in the nineteenth century. The two small wards must have been kept very busy.

APPENDIX 3

MENTAL DISORDER DIAGNOSES OF PATIENTS IN HANWELL ASYLUM, 1839

Mania	148
Melancholia	50
Monomania	4
Hypochondria	4
Incoherence	277
Dementia	137
Imbecility	171
Idiocy	14
Total number	805

All Hanwell's 805 patients were unshackled by Conolly within the first three months of his appointment as Medical Superintendent.

NOTES

1. 'Incoherence' was probably dementia as we use the term today, including general paralysis of the insane (now known to be a late result of syphilis infection) and was the cause for many diagnosed as incoherent, or possibly as a result of heavy metal (mercury, antimony etc) poisoning and other toxic hazards of the workplace in industrial London at that time.
2. 'Dementia' was used as a diagnosis for cases of acute

schizophrenia and other acute psychotic conditions. (See glossary).

3. The distinction between imbecility and idiocy was one of degree of mental incapacity, but often used interchangeably. (See glossary).

4. 'Monomania' is not a term in current use: it was probably used for those cases who generally functioned well mentally, but with fixed delusions, sometimes (but not always) as a consequence of previous syphilitic infection, and an early mental stage in the progression to GPI (general paralysis of the insane). (See glossary).

APPENDIX 4

Orders for Admission to Asylums (1845 Lunacy Act)

No pauper, or wandering lunatic, or lunatic neglected or cruelly treated by a relative, or other person, is to be received into any asylum, registered hospital or licensed house, without an order and statement according to the form and stating the particulars required in the form following, under the hands of one justice, or an officiating clergyman, with one of the overseers, or the relieving officer of the parish or union for which such pauper or other person shall be sent as aforesaid, nor without a medical certificate according to the form following, signed by one physician, surgeon, or apothecary, and dated not more than seven clear days previous to the reception of such patient.

ORDER FOR THE RECEPTION OF A PAUPER PATIENT

"I, C. D. [in the case of a justice of the peace], or we [in the case of a clergyman and relieving officer, &c.], the undersigned, having called to my [or 'our'] assistance a physician [or surgeon or apothecary, as the case may be], and having personally examined A.B., a pauper, and I, C.D. or we, [in the case of a clergyman and relieving officer &c.,] being satisfied that the said A.B. is a lunatic [or an insane person, or an idiot, or a person of unsound or imbecile mind] and a proper

person to be confined, I, or we [as the case may be], hereby direct you to receive the said A.B. as a patient into your asylum, hospital or house. Subjoined is a statement respecting the said A.B.
...(signed) (C.D.)

*A justice of the peace for the city or borough of ...[or an officiating clergyman of the parish of ...].
*The relieving officer of the union or parish of ...[or an overseer of the parish of...].

STATEMENT

Name of patient, and Christian name at length
Sex and age
Married, single, or widowed
Condition of life, and previous occupation (if any)
The religious persuasion, as far as is known
Previous place of abode
Length of time insane
Whether first attack
Age (if known) on first attack
Whether subject to epilepsy
Whether suicidal or dangerous to others
Previous places of confinement (if any)
I certify that to the best of my knowledge the above particulars are correctly stated
...(signed)
[To be signed by the relieving officer or overseer]

Dated the ...day of ...one thousand eight hundred and...
    To...Superintendent of the asylum for the county of ...or the lunatic hospital of ...or proprietor of the licensed house of ... [describing the asylum, hospital, or house].

FORM OF MEDICAL CERTIFICATE IN THE CASE OF PAUPER PATIENTS

"I, …being a fellow [or licentiate] of the Royal College of Physicians in London, [or a graduate in medicine of the university of … &c., or a member of the Royal College of Surgeons in London, or an Apothecary, duly authorized to practice by the Apothecaries Company in London,] hereby certify that I have this day personally examined A.B., the person named in the accompanying statement and order, and that the said A.B. is a lunatic [or an insane person, or an idiot, or a person of unsound or imbecile mind], and a proper person to be confined.

…(signed) Name

Place of abode.

Dated this…day of…one thousand eight hundred and…

…"

Every person who shall receive any pauper, or other such person, as before mentioned, into any asylum without such order and medical certificate, shall be deemed guilty of a misdemeanor.

NOTES: In the case of an insane person not a pauper, an order signed as before, accompanied by TWO medical certificates, each signed and dated by a medical man, not in partnership with the other, and who have each seen and examined the person named in the order separately from the other, and within not more than seven days prior to the reception of that person into an asylum.

APPENDIX 5

DAILY DIET IN THE HATTON ASYLUM

Bucknill's ascerbic – but honest – comment in 1858 was that 'the higher classes of society will improve by living somewhat below their average custom, and the lower classes by living above it'.

Throughout the nineteenth century the staple diet of the labouring poor was bread, butter (occasionally), potatoes, bacon, dilute beer, milk (again occasionally), while butcher's meat was eaten rarely and then usually in the form of offal. Many food items were adulterated.

Workhouse food was often adulterated because underpaid workhouse masters colluded with the suppliers and contractors to make the ingredients 'go further'.

Presumably the same applied – but possibly not – to asylums. Food adulteration generally was not suppressed until the 1872 Public Health Act.

A dietician's opinion is that the diet in the Hatton asylum (as printed below) whilst being somewhat monotonous, was reasonably well-balanced, if lacking in dairy produce; however, the patients' diet may well have been supplemented by dairy produce from the asylum's farms. In any event, it was undoubtedly considerably better than any obtaining outside the asylum for the labouring poor.

NB: soup for 100 patients, to be made of liquor if meat cooked the previous day, with 14 lb of leg or shin of beef, 7

215

lb peas, 6 lb rice, 3 lb scotch barley, 5 lb onions, salt, pepper and herbs.

EXTRAS: For men employed as ward-helpers or in outdoor labour, in the forenoon ½ pint beer; 2 oz bread; ½ oz cheese, and at 4pm ½ pint beer.

For women employed as ward-helpers or in kitchen or laundry, beer, bread, cheese in forenoon as for men.

The sick to be dieted at discretion of the Medical Superintendent.

MEN	WOMEN
Breakfast	
One pint of coffee	one pint of coffee
bread 6 oz; butter 3/8 oz	bread 5 oz; butter 3/8 oz
Dinner (Sun; Tue; Wed; Fri)	
cooked meat free from bone 5 ½ oz	cooked meat free from bone 4 ½ oz
bread 4 oz; beer ½ pint;	bread 4 oz; beer ½ pint;
veg about 12 oz	veg about 12 oz
Dinner (Mon; Thur)	
meat & potato pie-crust 12 oz	meat & potato pie-crust 12 oz
cooked meat 1½ oz	cooked meat 1½ oz
beer ½ pint	beer ½ pint
Dinner (Sat)	
soup 1 pint; bread 6 oz	soup 1 pint; bread 5 oz
beer ½ pint	beer ½ pint
Supper	
bread 6 oz; cheese 2 oz	bread 5 oz; butter 3/8 oz
½ pint beer OR	one pint of tea
bread 6 oz; butter 3/8 oz	
one pint of tea	

APPENDIX 6

Occupations of the 1356 patients admitted to the Hatton Asylum during WHP's tenure (1852 – 1884)

Agricultural pupil	1
Artist	1
Accountant	2
Barber	1
Barmaid	7
Basket maker	6
Baker	12
Bath chair man	4
Beehouse keeper	2
Betting man	2
Blacksmith	13
Boatman	14
Boatwoman	2
Boilermaker	2
Bookbinder	2
Bookkeeper	2
Brass founder	6
Brass hinge dresser	3
Bricklayer	23
Brickmaker	9
Broker	2
Builder	1

Butcher	20
Button maker	3
Butler	4
Comm traveler	2
Cab driver	2
Cab maker	3
Canal lockkeeper	1
Candlestick maker	1
Cap maker 1 Carpenter	38
Carrier	4
Carter	2
Cattle herder	1
Chair maker	3
Charwoman	45
Chimney sweep	3
China dealer	1
Clerk	33
Cloth worker	1
Coachman	7
Compositor	2
Coachmaker	2
Coal checker	8
Coal heaver	2
Coal merchant	21
Comb maker	2
Compactor	2
Cook	9
Confectioner	2
Cooper	1
Cotton winder	2
Cow keeper	2
Currier	1
Discharged soldier	36

Domestic (wives)	596
Draper's assistant	11
Dressmaker	44
Drover	4
Dyer	7
Edge tool maker	1
Engineer	6
Engine driver	3
Excise man	2
Family bailiff	2
Farmer	35
Farrier	3
Filecutter	2
Fieldman	2
Fisherman's asst	1
Fitter	2
Flour salesman	1
Fly driver	2
Flint setter	2
Gamekeeper	3
Gas worker	3
Gardener	24
Gas fitter	4
Gentleman	1
Glover	1
Gov't agent	1
Governess	14
Gravedigger	1
Greengrocer	1
Grocer/Assistant	12
Grinder	1

Groom	14
Gun finisher	3
Harness maker	1
Hatter	3
Hawker	21
Hay tyer	1
Hirer of bicycles	1
Horse breaker	3
Housekeeper	16
Huntsman	3
Innkeeper	11
Ironmonger	5
Iron turner	1
Jeweller	2
Joiner	2
Labourer	477
Laundress	42
Lacemaker	1
Lace dresser	1
Letter carrier	2
Licenced victualler	1
Lodgings keeper	3
Lithographer	2
Machinist	5
Mail driver	1
Maltster	2
Mason	10
Maths instr. Maker	1
Med. Practitioner	2

Merchant	2
Midwife	1
Milkman	2
Milkseller	1
Miller	6
Milliner	3
Monthly nurses	3
Mountebank	1
Musician	5
Nail cutter	2
Nun (professed)	1
Needlemaker	25
None known	168
Nurse	11
Omnibus prop	1
Outfitter apprentice	1
Painter	12
Paper box maker	1
Paint clerk	2
Pig dealer	2
Plasterer	7
Plumber	4
Photographer	1
Policeman	2
Porter	5
Postmaster	1
Press worker	1
Printer	5
Prostitute	4
Publican	7
Puddler	1

Pump maker	1
Pupil teacher	2
Railway clerk	3
Railway servant	12
Railway agent	2
Rail carriage maker	1
Rate Collector	2
Relieving officer	1
Saddler	2
Saddle stitcher	1
Sailor	8
Sawyer	2
Schoolmaster	6
Schoolmistress	6
Script reader	1
Scanner	1
Servant	327
Shepherd	5
Shoesmith	2
Shoe binder	9
Shoemaker	51
Shop woman	3
Silk winder	53
Silversmith	1
Slater	1
Soda water infuser	1
Solicitor	1
Spade maker	1
Spirit dealer	1
Stay maker	1
Stocking maker	12
Stoker	3

Striker	3
Slate quarrier	2
Tailor	38
Tallow chandler	1
Tea dealer	1
Timber dealer	1
Tin man	1
Tobacco seller	1
Toll clerk	1
Tramp	4
Turning hand	3
Trunk maker	1
Tutor	1
Toymaker	2
Upholsterer	3
Umbrella maker	1
Waggoner	1
Waitress	1
Warehouseman	3
Warehousewoman	1
Watchmaker	49
Weaver	153
Weaver harness mkr	1
Wheelwright	11
Whitesmith	5
Wood carver	1
Wood turner	2
TOTAL:	1356

APPENDIX 7

PATIENTS & STAFF OF THE HATTON ASYLUM – THE
FIRST 100 YEARS: STATISTICS COLLECTED FOR THE
CENTENARY CELEBRATIONS IN 1952

Male admissions	12,556
Female admissions	15,778
Total	28,334
Male discharges	7,495
Female discharges	10,381
Total	18,876
Male deaths	4,466
Female deaths	4,600
Total	9,066
Male discharges + deaths	11,961
Female discharges + deaths	14,981
Total	26,942
Total admissions	28,334
Total discharges + deaths	26,942
Total on books (29 June 1952)	1,392
Full time staff	323
Part time staff	108
Total	*431*

YEARS OF SERVICE OF STAFF (as of 28th June 1952):

40+ years	4	1.24%
30+ years	20	6.19%
25+ years	47	14.23%
20+ years	76	22.4%
15+ years	118	36.5%
10+ years	154	48.2%

The longest surviving member of staff (as of 28th June 1952) was the head gardener (47 years), and the other members with 40+ years of service were the Night Superintendent (46 years), the coalman (45 years) and a Charge Nurse [senior qualified male nurse] (43 years).

Those with 30+ years of service included the drains manager, the head vegetable gardener, the blacksmith, a Ward Sister, a Staff Nurse [senior qualified female nurse] and seven Charge Nurses.

Apart from a substantial number of Staff Nurses and Charge Nurses with 20+ years of service – as one might expect – others included a wheelwright, a stoker, a housekeeper, a driver, a female cook, a mattress maker, a painter, a foreman bricklayer and a foreman joiner: all very much part of the spectrum of occupations to be expected within any large institution or small village community or large institution.

Almost half the workforce had at least 10 years service.

APPENDIX 8

McNaghten Rules

In 1843, Daniel McNaghten, who believed he was being persecuted by the Tory Party, attempted to assassinate the Prime Minister Sir Robert Peel, but in error shot and killed his Private Secretary, Edward Drummond. At his trial he was acquitted of murder 'by reason of insanity'. There was some public disquiet following this verdict, and the 'McNaghten Rules' were drawn up by the House of Lords for use in future trials where insanity was being offered as a defence. They state:

1. "Every man [and woman] is presumed to be sane and responsible for their crimes unless the contrary is proved"
2. "To establish a defence on the grounds of insanity, it must be proved that at the time of committing the act the party accused was labouring under such a defect of reason from disease of the mind, as not to know the nature and quality of the act he was doing, or if he did know it, that he did not know he was doing what was wrong".

So, WHP would have been asked to give his opinion on three questions:

- Is mental illness present?

- Is the alleged criminal act a product of the mental illness?
- How did the mental illness cause the defendant to commit the alleged crime?

Although the judge could direct the jury, it was ultimately the jury's responsibility to determine guilt.

APPENDIX 9

REPORT OF TRIAL AT WARWICK CROWN COURT 18
FEBRUARY 1882
FROM THE LEAMINGTON SPA COURIER
(18 FEBRUARY 1882):

CHARGE OF MANSLAUGHTER AGAINST AN ASYLUM ATTENDANT-James Hughes, asylum attendant, was indicted for the manslaughter of David Pullan, an inmate of the Birmingham Borough Lunatic Asylum, on 13th October, 1881. Mr Soden and Mr Cartland prosecuted, and Mr Colmore and Mr Fitzgerald defended the prisoner. On Monday, the 10th October, the deceased was admitted to the Birmingham Borough Asylum. He was then in delicate health, suffering from spinal disease and stricture of the bladder. During the night he was fairly well, and on the Tuesday prisoner came on as attendant in the dormitory he was placed in. Prisoner complained to the superintendent that the deceased would not allow himself to be dressed, and he was told to let him wait a little longer in bed. According to the evidence for the prosecution prisoner shortly afterwards dragged deceased out of bed. A struggle ensued, deceased was knocked down, and prisoner struck him with his fists on the ribs. Later in the morning prisoner kicked the deceased on the chest while he was in the gallery. Shortly afterwards he was observed to be in a state of collapse. He had evidently received some injury, as he had a mark across his nose. He became unconscious, and continued in that state till the Thursday, when he died. A post-mortem examination of the body showed the cause of death to have been pneumonia, the result of rupture of the bladder. It was contended by the prosecutors that this

229

rupture had been caused by the violence of prisoner. After evidence had been given, Mr Colmore submitted that there was no case to go to the jury. His Lordship, while not seeing his way to take the case out of the hands of the jury, after reviewing the evidence, suggested to the jury that they should dismiss the charge on the medical evidence. This the jury adopted at once, and Hughes was dismissed. His Lordship afterwards expressed his acquiescence in their conduct, and said he believed death was the result of an accident.

APPENDIX 10

THE SHOWER-BATH AS A TREATMENT OF INSANITY

The bath was a contraption comprising a closed bath, some 26 inches in diameter, with a perforated zinc plate 14 inches in diameter about nine feet from the floor through which water fell at a rate of nine gallons/minute. The amount of water falling on a patient's head would be about four gallons. Males were treated for up to one minute; females for up to half a minute.

Dr John Campbell, the Assistant Medical Superintendent of Garlands Asylum, Carlisle, provided a personal recommendation in the Journal of Psychiatry, January 1873:

I have on several occasions taken a shower-bath in the bath and in my opinion the effects of the shower-bath are greatly superior to those of the ordinary cold bath; the shock is greater, and also the reaction and the feeling of muscular activity and exhilaration of spirits, which are experienced after a shower-bath and a vigorous rubbing down are what many people would hardly believe until they had tried it.

It is considered to be especially good for hysterical mania in girls and in cases where persistent excitement exists without organic cause.

ABBREVIATIONS

AMO	Assistant Medical Officer
AMOAHI	Association of Medical Officers of Asylums and Hospitals for the Insane
b	born
BA	Bachelor of Arts
BAO	Batchelor in Obstetrics
BCh /BChir	Batchelor of Surgery
BJ Psych	British Journal of Psychiatry
BMA	British Medical Association
BMJ	British Medical Journal
BS	Batchelor of Surgery
Cantab	University of Cambridge
COD	Concise Oxford Dictionary
CRO	County Records Office
d	died
DC	death certificate
DCL	Doctor of Civil Law (Oxford University honorary degree)
DUFC	Dublin University Football Club
FRCP	Fellow of the Royal College of Physicians
FRCS	Fellow of the Royal College of Surgeons
GMC	General Medical Council
GMR	General Medical Register
KCH	King's College Hospital
LLD	Doctor of Law (Oxford University)
LRCP	Licentiate of the Royal College of Physicians

LRCS	Licentiate of the Royal College of Surgeons
LSA	Licentiate of the Society of Apothecaries
m	married
MA	Master of Arts
MB/BM	Batchelor of Medicine
MCC	Marylebone Cricket |Club
MD	Doctor of Medicine
MPS	Medico-Psychological Association
MRCP	Member of the Royal College of Physicians
MRCPsych	Member of the Royal College of Psychiatrists
MRCS	Member of the Royal College of Surgeons
MS	Master of Surgery /Medical Superintendent
Oxon	University of Oxford
q	qualified
RHA	Royal Hibernian Association
TCD	Trinity College, Dublin (Dublin University)
UCH	University College Hospital
UCL	University College, London
WCCC	Warwickshire County Cricket Club
WHP	William Henry Parsey

GLOSSARY

Imbecile	Of moderately reduced mental capacity since birth or an early age but of slightly higher mental capacity than an idiot. A cretin would also be included in this all-embracing term. In fact idiot and imbecile were used indiscriminately, even by alienists.
Inmate	A term commonly used for residents in asylums: the description 'patient' is traditionally used in medical circles ('client', or 'service user' in modern social services parlance).
Insane person	A synonym for 'lunatic': in common usage in nineteenth Century, but now avoided in favour of diagnosis of the specific mental disorder.
Lunatic	An insane person, often of normal intelligence, who through mental, physical or metabolic disease has descended into madness, with the possibility of recovery in some cases (in earlier times thought to be influenced by the phases of the moon as was epilepsy).
Madhouse	A private dwelling for the care of insane persons, maintained for the personal profit of the proprietor (medical or otherwise), and usually resorting therein to using physical restraint to a greater or lesser degree to manage the residents.

Mad-Doctor	A term used in the 18th Century (and earlier) for those doctors, often with no particular special expertise (and often only a pecuniary interest) in the care of the insane, who were proprietors of 'madhouses' in which a number of insane persons would temporarily or permanently reside, cared for by a variable number of attendants.
Mania	As we use the term today – a condition affecting all aspects of understanding, and being totally unresponsive to reason, with extreme excitability and loss of self-control.
Melancholia	Considered by the Ancients to be due to a bodily imbalance of black bile (one of the four humours – blood, phlegm, yellow bile and black bile), but now referred to as depressive illness (often recurrent) and considered to be biological, for the main part, and of varying degrees of severity, but often with a spontaneous resolution for many sufferers (in the fullness of time); modern medication can reduce the severity of an episode of illness and also hasten recovery for many sufferers.
Monomania	A fixed delusion (or 'idée fixe' – it was first described by Esquirol in France) in an otherwise sane and mentally normally balanced person e.g. Captain Ahab's obsession with pursuing and killing the whale Moby Dick.

Moral insanity	Abnormal emotions and behaviour in the apparent absence of intellectual impairment, delusions or hallucinations. It was a subjective diagnosis in the nineteenth Century (a Dictionary of Psychological Medicine of 1856 takes two pages to try to define the term) which allowed committal to the asylum of the socially deviant, or just plainly unmanageable, where mental illness was not necessarily evident. Very much a term allowing for abuse of the committal procedure, and en used very much more often in the 20th Century for cases of (repeated) illegitimate pregnancy, or simply wilful or ungovernable members of the family (usually female).
Neurosis	Minor disorders of behaviour, in the absence of intellectual impairment, e.g. anxiety, phobias, hysteria. Frequently found in young women, and considered to be the domain of the physician, and not the alienist, in the nineteenth century. In the 20th century onwards, the 'talking treatment' of Freud and the psycho-analysts was the mainstay of (often protracted) treatment. Today CBT (Cognitive Behavioural Therapy) is the treatment of choice. Medication can be helpful too.
Non-pauper lunatic	Not necessarily rich, but theoretically obliged to fund own provision of care in a privately run 'mad-house'. Sometimes received into the Hatton Asylum (and others) at a slightly higher weekly charge (paid by the family) than that paid by paupers, (thus maintaining the class distinction for patient and family, no doubt), should the asylum's capacity so allow.

Pauper lunatic	Poor, and unable to pay any asylum fees directly, so maintained in the asylum out of the Parish's finances, obtained from the poor rate.
Psychosis	Severe mental disorder characterized by a loss of contact with reality, involving delusions, hallucinations (visual or auditory) and often violent behaviour directed towards either themselves or others.
Unsound mind	An all-embracing term that includes any person incapable of managing their own affairs: this includes idiots, imbeciles those with acquired mental defect, and those lacking mental capacity to go to trial (see Appendix 8).

BIBLIOGRAPHY

Allderidge, Patricia 'A cat surpassing in beauty, and other therapeutic animals' *Psych Bulletin* (1991), 15, 759-82

Allderidge, Patricia 'Hospitals, Madhouses and Asylums: cycles in the care of the insane' *B J Psych* (1979), 134, 321-34

Andrews, Jonathan & Scull, Andrew *Undertaker of the Mind: John Monro and Mad-Doctoring in Eighteenth Century England,* University of California Press (2002)

Arton, Michael *The Professionalisation of Mental Health Nursing in Great Britain 1850-1950* PhD thesis University College London (1986)

Ashton, Rosemary *Victorian Bloomsbury* Yale University Press (2012)

Bateman, Sir Frederick & Rye, Walter *The History of the Bethel at Norwich* Gibbs and Walter Norwich (1906)

Browne, William AF *What Asylums Were, Are and Ought to Be* Black Edinburgh (1837)

Bucknill, John Charles *The Mad Folk of Shakespeare* MacMillan & Co London (1867)

Bucknill, John Charles *Notes on Asylums for the Insane in America* J & A Churchill London (1876)

Campbell, John 'The Shower-bath in Insanity' *B J Psych* Jan 1873, 18 (84) 543-548

Clark, James *A Memoir of John Conolly MD* John Murray London (1869)

Clarkson, Josiah *The Nerves of The Chest. Warneford Prize Essay 1843* John Churchill London (1845)

Conolly, John *An Inquiry Concerning the Indications of Insanity: with suggestions for the better protection and care of the insane* John Taylor London (1830)

Conolly, John *On The Construction and Government of Lunatic Asylums and Hospitals for the Insane* Churchill London (1857)

Conolly, John *The Treatment of the Insane without Mechanical Restraints* Smith, Eccles & Co London (1856)

Conolly, John *A Study of Hamlet* Edward Moxon & Co London (1863)

Cumming, William Fullerton *Notes on Lunatic Asylums in Germany: and Other Parts of Europe* John Churchill London (1852)

Elston, Mary Ann *Women Doctors in the British Health Services: a sociological study* PhD thesis University of Leeds (1986)

Gardiner Hill, Robert *A Lecture on the Management of Lunatic Asylums and the Treatment of the Insane; delivered at the Mechanics' Institution, Lincoln, on the 21ˢᵗ June 1838* Simpkin, Marshall & Co London (1838)

Hughes, Thomas *'Tom Brown's Schooldays' by an Old Boy* J Palmer Cambridge for MacMillan & Co (1857)

Hunt, Margaret et al, *Central Hospital Remembered* S Warwickshire Mental Health Trust (1998).

Jones, Kathleen *Asylums and After* Athlone Press London (1993)

Joyce, James *Ulysses* Penguin London (2000)

Langley, Anne *Warwick County Asylum, the first reformatory outside London* Stretton-on-Dunsmore History Society (2006)

Lethbridge, JP *Foul Deeds and Suspicious Deaths in Warwickshire* Wharncliffe Books Barnsley (2007)

Lowe, Louisa *The Bastilles of England; or, the Lunacy Laws at Work* Crookenden & Co London (1883)

Macalpine, Ida & Hunter, Richard *George III and the Mad Business* Allen Lane London (1969)

May, Trevor *The Victorian Workhouse* Shire Publications Oxford (2009)

Parry-Jones, William *The Trade in Lunacy* Routledge & Kegan Paul London (1972)

Pratt, Anna *Seven Months in the Kingston Lunatic Asylum* Jordan & Osborn Kingston Jamaica (1860)

Rivington, Walter *The Medical Profession* Fannin & Co Dublin (1879)

Rutherford, Sarah 'Landscapes for the Mind', *J Warks Gardens Trust*, Autumn (2002)

Spratley, Violet A and Stern, Edward S *History of the Mental Hospital at Hatton in the County of Warwick* Hatton (1952)

Stern, Edward *Three Notable Nineteenth Century Psychiatrists of Warwickshire* BJ Psych (1961) 107 (447) 187-193

Tromans, Nicholas *Richard Dadd: the Artist and the Asylum* Tate Publishing London (2011)

Tuke, Daniel Hack and Bicknill, John *A Manual of Psychological Medicine*

Blanchard and Lea Philadelphia (1858)

Wade, Charles *The History of the Leamington Tennis Court Club 1846-1996* Ronaldson Publications Oxford (1996)

ARCHIVES

Warwick County Lunatic Asylum archive [CR 1664] CRO Warwick

Parliamentary Papers

Metropolitan Commissioners in Lunacy Reports

JOURNALS

British Journal of Psychiatry

British Medical Journal

Journal of the Royal College of Physicians

Journal of the Warwickshire Gardens Trust

Psychiatric Bulletin

NEWSPAPERS

Royal Leamington Spa Courier

WEBSITES

British National Formulary www.bnf.org
Langdondownmuseum.org.uk
Munk's Roll, Royal College of Physicians
Museumofthemind.org.uk
Roberts,A, Social Science History, Middlesex University, London,
www.studymore.org.uk
Royal College of Psychiatrists online website

INDEX

WHP = William Henry Parsey

knighted 61; dies and buried in Stretton-on-Dunsmore, Warks 61
Commissioners in Lunacy, 16; statutory duties 16; rules regarding selection of asylum sites 20; advice regarding asylum design 22
Conolly, Dr John, birth in Market Rasen 37; marries Elizabeth Collins 37; lives in Tours, France 37; MD Edinburgh University 38; enters general practice in Stratford-upon-Avon 38; involved with establishing dispensaries in Stratford and Warwick 39; elected alderman 41; becomes 'Inspecting Physician to lunatic houses of Warwickshire' 41; opinion of 'madhouses' in Warwickshire 18; appointed 'Professor of the Treatment of Diseases' at UCL 42; resigns and returns to Warwickshire 43; helps found BMA 44; helps found Warwick Natural History Society 45; visits Dr Gardiner Hill in Lincoln 11; appointed Physician to Hanwell asylum 47; abolishes restraint in asylum 48; honorary doctorate in Civil Law (DCL) Oxford University 50; retires, but continues as Visiting Physician 51; writes pamphlet on Hamlet's madness 51; visits Hatton asylum 51; dies and buried in Hanwell Cemetery 51; marble bust presented to Royal College of Physicians 51

County Asylum Act 1845, 15
Cumberland & Westmoreland Asylum, 15

Devon County Lunatic Asylum, 11, 36, 53, 72
Dispensaries, Stratford-upon-Avon 39, 40; Warwick 39; Leamington 68
Dickins, Rev Thomas Bourne, chaplain to Hatton asylum 158n39; receives LL D Cambridge University 165n81; presents gift and appreciative letter to WHP 168n92
Darwin, Charles, 167n87
Down, Dr John Langdon, 124, 128
Down's Syndrome 128 n2

Earlswood Asylum *see* Down, Dr John Langdon
Edinburgh University, 37, 38
Esquirol, Jean-Etienne, 3

Forbes, Dr John, 38, 62n14

Gardiner Hill, Dr Robert, asylum in Lincoln 11; first physician to abolish restraint in England 11
George III, King, first lapse into insanity 4; illness probably porphyria 5; church built to celebrate recovery 5; scurrilous poem about his physicians 5
Gheel community, model of 'family care' of lunatics 54

Handel, George Friderick, 14n15; 119n2
Hanwell asylum *see* Middx County Lunatic Asylum
Hastings, Dr Charles *see* British